Landbeach

Bird Atlas

by
Geoffrey Kelly

Published by
Norfolk and Norwich
Naturalists' Society

Occasional Publication No. 1

© Geoffrey I. Kelly 1986

ISBN 0 9591130 1 8

First published in 1986 by the Norfolk and Norwich Naturalists' Society

Printed and bound in Great Britain by Witley Press Ltd., Hunstanton, Norfolk.

Contents

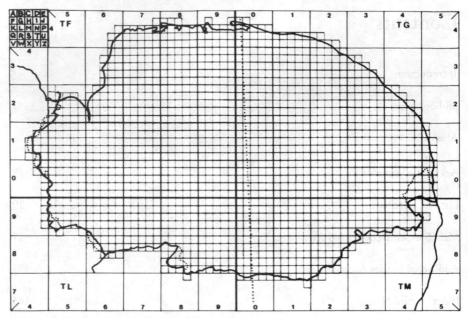

Map 1: Norfolk Tetrads and the National Grid

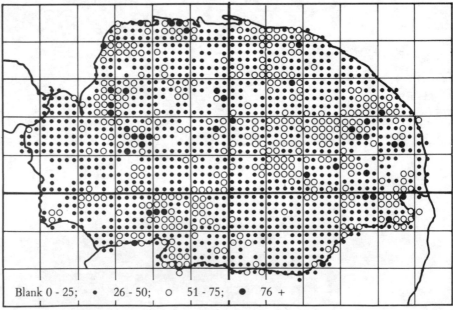

Blank 0 - 25;　●　26 - 50;　○　51 - 75;　●　76 +

Map 2: Species Richness of Individual Tetrads

4

Introduction

The *Norfolk Bird Atlas* is the culmination of six years of fieldwork — from 1980 to 1985 — by over 200 recorders. This fieldwork, the Norfolk Breeding Bird Survey, was organised on much the same basis as other county atlas schemes for which the results have already been published, for instance B.D. Harding's *Bedfordshire Bird Atlas* (1979) and the Kent Ornithological Society's *Birds of Kent* (1981), as well as in respect of others still in progress or in the planning stage. That is, the county was divided into recording units called tetrads, these being the 2-km X 2-km squares formed by the even numbered lines of the Ordnance Survey's national grid system. Including those which overlap the county boundary, Norfolk has 1,455 tetrads, and within these observers were given the task of establishing which birds bred, or otherwise probably or possibly bred, during the survey period. See Map 1 for the relationship of tetrads to the national grid.

In all, 61,000 records were submitted by observers — an average of 42 birds per tetrad. Naturally, there were wide variations in the species richness of individual tetrads (ignoring the fact that some coastal ones only included small areas of land). These variations were not only due to the fact that some tetrads contained a wider range of habitats than others, and hence attracted more breeding species, but also to the fact that some squares were thoroughly covered in each season of the project while some were only given a single visit in the last year of the survey. Nevertheless, in the last cited instances a reasonable impression of the breeding birds present was always gathered so no square was left seriously 'underdone'. Map 2 provides an indication of the species richness of each tetrad.

Observers, who handled from one to over one hundred tetrads each (and who in any case sometimes worked in pairs or small teams), were given a recording card for each one of these. Upon each card was printed the names of all the birds it had been thought likely would be found in the county as a whole. By each species' name were columns relating to categories of possible, probable and confirmed breeding; the observer concerned would indicate the nature of finds in the relevant column, while aiming to achieve as high a category as possible for each species by the end of the survey. The categories were to be codified within each column according to a scheme devised for the BTO/IWC *Atlas of Breeding Birds in Britain and Ireland* project of 1968-1972 (organised upon a 10-km square recording unit), viz.:

Col 1 — *Possible Breeding*
✔ — Bird recorded in breeding season in possible nesting habitat

Col 2 — *Probable Breeding*
S — Singing Male
T — Bird apparently on territory
D — Display or agitated behaviour
N — Visiting probable nest-site
B — Nest building

Col 3 — *Confirmed Breeding*
DD — Distraction display
UN — Used nest found
FL — Recently fledged young
FS — Adult carrying faecal sac
FY — Adult with food for young
ON — Adult entering/leaving likely nest-site
NE — Nest and eggs/bird sitting tight
NY — Nest and young or downy young

The cards supplied to observers were generally satisfactory, although no records were forthcoming for three species printed upon them — Corncrake, Little Gull and Black Tern. Conversely, records were submitted for a number of other species — rarities and introductions — but blank spaces had been left on the cards to allow for these. Some observers asked for certain records to be treated confidentially, and these requests have been honoured — some of them in any case relating to species which are not mapped for security reasons. Otherwise, where a record or records has or have been omitted from a map the fact is indicated in the text. In respect of two species, Sparrowhawk and Little Tern, a degree of security was observed by mapping them on a 10-km square, rather than a tetrad, basis.

All records submitted were considered to have been made in good faith, and in only a handful of cases did their accuracy have to be queried. Such cases tended to concern 'slips of the pen' by observers on their recording cards. A few records of scarce or rare birds may have been accepted for the *Norfolk Bird Atlas* without their having been vetted by the British Bird's Rarities Committee: submission of such records to this body, although desirable, was not a pre-condition of their acceptance by the present work. Although information concerning confidential submissions or sensitive species cannot be released, readers spotting errors or omissions — of which it is hoped there are but few — are invited to contact the author c/o Natural History Dept., Castle Museum, Norwich, NR1 3JU.

Norfolk is arguably the finest county in mainland Britain for ornithological interest, one with a long and honourable tradition of conservation epitomised in a superb range of reserves. Space is at a premium in these introductory paragraphs and there is no room for a perhaps desirable analysis of the county's natural, semi-natural and man-made habitats. However, Maps 3-6 indicate many features which have influenced the distribution of breeding birds. They may assist readers in a discovery of correspondences, only some of which are considered in the main text of this work.

Bearing in mind the relationship of individual tetrads to each 10-km square (see Map 1), records are plotted on the main maps according to the following conventions:

•   Possible breeding   o   Probable breeding   ●   Confirmed breeding

The text which follows for each species gives the vernacular and scientific names, followed by a numerical and percentage based breakdown of its prevalence and the categories of breeding evidence submitted. (Percentages given for these three categories are rounded to the nearest whole number, and may therefore add up to 99% or 101%). Then comes a consideration of the bird's status as suggested by the Norfolk Breeding Bird Survey and, when appropriate, from other recent and historic evidence. In respect of further points raised, it is hoped that those clearly expressed as conjectural will trigger discussion and perhaps initiate further research.

BIBLIOGRAPHY

Harding, B. D. *Bedfordshire bird atlas.* Luton: Bedfordshire Natural History Society. 1979.

Kent Ornithological Society *Birds of Kent.* Meopham: Kent Ornithological Society, 1981.

Riviere, B. B. *A history of the birds of Norfolk.* London: Witherby. 1930.

Seago, M. J. *Birds of Norfolk.* Norwich: Jarrold. 1967, and revd. ed. 1977.

Seago, M. J. (ed.) Norfolk bird reports, 1976-1985. *Transactions of the Norfolk and Norwich Naturalists' Society.*

Sharrock, J. T. R. *The atlas of breeding birds in Britain and Ireland.* Berkhamsted: Poyser for British Trust for Ornithology and Irish Wildbird Conservancy. 1976. — cited as BTO/IWC *Atlas.*

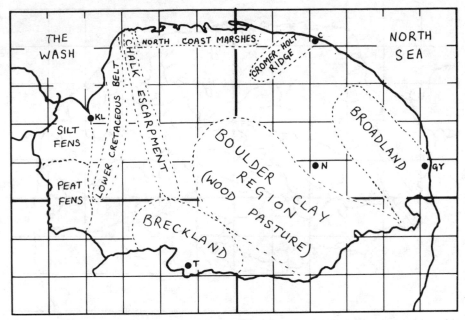

Map 3: Norfolk's Natural History Regions

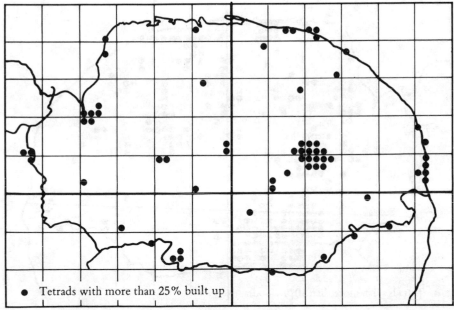

● Tetrads with more than 25% built up

Map 4: Norfolk's Larger Towns and Villages

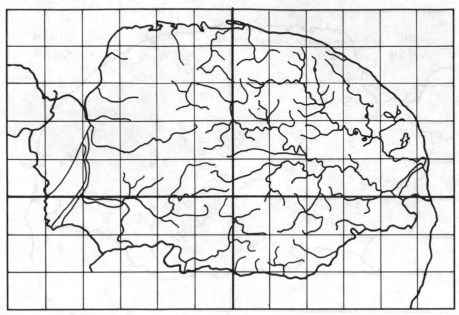

Map 5: Norfolk's Waterways

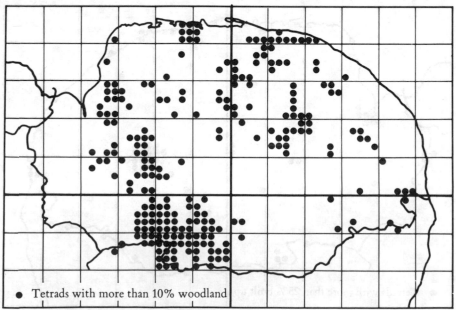

● Tetrads with more than 10% woodland

Map 6: Norfolk's Principal Woodlands

8

ABBREVIATIONS

BTO/IWC = British Trust for Ornithology/Irish Wildbird Conservancy
NarVOS   = Nar Valley Ornithological Society
NBBS   = Norfolk Breeding Bird Survey
NBR   = Norfolk Bird Report
NNNS   = Norfolk and Norwich Naturalists' Society
RSPB   = Royal Society for the Protection of Birds

Acknowledgements

First and foremost, the author and publisher acknowledge the major role B.D. Harding played in getting the NBBS off the ground and co-ordinating its activities for the first three years of its six year duration. Without his having persuaded the Norfolk and Norwich Naturalists' Society to foster this project, the *Norfolk Bird Atlas* would not have appeared.

The author, having undertaken fieldwork throughout the NBBS, took over its direction for both the second half of its course and in respect of collating the total data input. This he could not have done without the constant support, advice and occasional chauffeuring of John Goldsmith of the Norwich Castle Museum Natural History Department. John's colleagues, Tony Irwin and Rob Driscoll, also gave active support — in particular, during the preparation of this present work.

John O'Sullivan and Chris Durdin of the RSPB Regional Office, Norwich, gave this project their unstinting support; they also advised in respect of the treatment of sensitive species in the *Norfolk Bird Atlas*. Finally, they kindly arranged financial assistance regarding the author's travelling expenses in much of the peat Fens of South-west Norfolk — an area for which it proved difficult to find observers willing to carry out fieldwork.

The BTO's Norfolk representatives, Alec Bull and Moss Taylor, were helpful in many ways; in particular, they arranged for relevant data from the BTO surveys which they directed during the NBBS to be transmitted to this scheme's files. J.B. Kemp and Mrs E.D. Parrinder also passed on data from special projects: in particular re Long-eared Owl and Little Ringed Plover.

Special thanks are due to Michael Seago, Norfolk County Bird Recorder, for his assistance in a number of ways. The Council of the Norfolk and Norwich Naturalists' Society encouraged this project and the Society has undertaken the publication of this *Atlas*. David Fagg assisted greatly with the final production, while several Society members helped with the production of maps. Graham Easy, Richard Millington, Dick Jones and Malcolm Ausden contributed the vignettes.

In the list which follows of contributors to the NBBS, it is hoped that no active worker for the project has been inadvertently missed. The work of all these volunteers has been valued greatly: however, apart from the author, John Goldsmith, Barry Hudson and Ian Simper might be singled out as those who performed the sterling task of surveying fifty or more tetrads.

Geoffrey Ian Kelly   September 1986

List of Contributors

R.M. Aldrich
P.R. Allard
T. Allen
R. Andrews
D. Archer
P. Banwell
Mrs J. Barns
P.J. Barron
S.R. Beal
M. Bean
Miss S. Bean
Rev. G.D.R. Bell
R. Bentley
J.M. Birtwell
Sqdn. Ldr. M.J. Blair
Mrs M. Bocking
G.S. Bowen
Mrs M.A. Brewster
BTO
Maj.-Gen. R.S. Broke
A. Browne
G. Buck
D.W. Buckingham
A.L. Bull
E.F. Campbell
B. Cannell
Dr and Mrs K.J. Carlson
B. Carman
H. Caswell
P. Caswell
P.J. Cawley
H. Chandler
J. Charman
R. Chestney
D. Chilvers
Miss C.M.A. Chinn
Mr and Mrs P.R. Clarke
Mrs S. Cooper
P. Cornelleson
Hon. B. Cozens-Hardy
E.J. Cross
C.M. Davidson
J.A. and J.H. Dawson
D.A. Dorling
Miss E.M Dorling
R.J. Driscoll
C. Durdin
J.F. Durdin
H. Easwell
J. Eaton
P. Etherington
L. Evans
R. Eve
M.R. Farnham
F.J.L. Farrow
P.C. Feakes
Miss M. Fearns

R.J. Fisher
R. Fletcher
Mrs O. Fowler
N. Gallichan
C. Gibson
Mr and Mrs J.G. Goldsmith
P. Gotham
R. Gribble
Mrs B. Griffin
J. Gudgeon
Mrs R. Hadnam
Mrs C. Haines
P. Hall
R.C. Hancy
Mr and Mrs B.D. Harding
S. Harris
D.A. Henshilwood
G.F. Hibberd
P.J. Higgins
T. Hill
D.A. Holmes
C. Holt
T. Holzer
D.T. Horsley
G. Howell
T. Howes
T.J. Howlett
B. Hudson
D. Hudson
A.W. Humphrey
Dr A.G. Irwin
A.W. James
A.R. Jenkins
A.E. Johnson
R. Jones
Mr and Mrs R. Joslin
G. Keele
P. Keeler
G.I. Kelly
C.P. Kelsey
Dr D. Kelsey
J.B. Kemp
Dr I.F. Keymer
R.E. Kimber
J. Kirk
P. Kitchener
N.A. Knight
Mr and Mrs M. Knights
Mrs S. Lake
P.W. Lambley
A.J. Last
M.E. Laxen
M.P. Lee
I. Leggett
Dr J. Lines
Mrs M.J. Littlewood
T. Lockwood

Mrs R. Ludlow
Dr P.A. McAnulty
B.J. Madden
O. Marks
B. Martin
G. Martin
R. Massingham
Miss D.M. Maxey
C. Read
M.R. Meechem
Mrs J. Metcalf
Mr and Mrs J.S. Mighell
N.H. Moore
R.M.C. Moore
J. Morris
H. Moy
J. Moyes
Mr and Mrs C. Mussell
NarVOS
C. Neale
D.G. Neale
Deaconess M. Newton
R.D. Nichols
G. Nobes
Mrs R. Northall
Norwich Wildlife Group
S. Organ
J. O'Sullivan
D.L. Ovenden
Lt.-Col. T.H. Pares
D. Palmer
R. Parfitt
Mr and Mrs M. Parker
Mrs E.D. Parrinder
F.H. Pigg
P. Pratley
B. Pummell
J. Raincock
M. Rains
M. Read
C. Regan
M. Ridgard
R. Robinson
RSPB
C. Rutter
K. Saul
V. Scipp
M.J. Seago
J. Shorten
Mrs R. Shrive
Dr J.C.B. Shutes
K. Simmonds
I.J. Simper
R.M. Skelton
C. Slater
Miss J.E. Smith
K. Smith

M. Smith
M.F. Smith
M. Softley
S. South
M.A. Spriggs
K. Stedman
STANTA Bird Group
K. Swift
Miss K.E. Tarsey
Dr M.P. Taylor
W. Thrower
D.W. Titterington
Mrs R. Tooley
P. Varney
A.E. Vine
J.E. Walker
I. White
J.R. Whitelegg
Wildfowl Trust
Mrs J. Willey
J.F. and A.M. Wilson
Mrs J.M. Womersley
M. Wood
M.E. Wood
T. Wright
R.E. Young

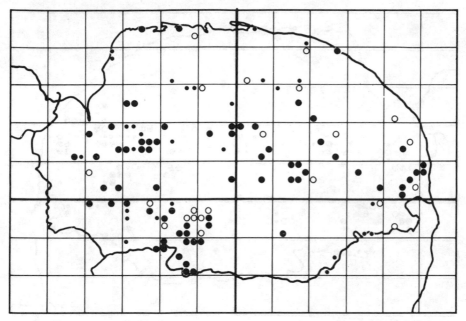

Little Grebe

Tachybaptus ruficollis

Tetrads recorded in:	122	(8%)
Possible breeding:	31	(25%)
Probable breeding:	22	(18%)
Confirmed breeding:	69	(57%)

A not uncommon breeding species, with most records originating from flooded gravel pits, ponds, lakes and Breckland meres. Breeding was also established along drains flanking the Nar and Little Ouse rivers, as well as in dykes behind the southern 'Walls' of Breydon Water and in Haddiscoe 'Island'. Very few records were forthcoming from the Fens or from Broadland proper. Gravel pits and other waters in the valleys of the Yare, Wensum, Wissey and Nar held both Little and Great Crested Grebes in some instances; the former species was found to favour smaller sheets of water for the most part.

Most records of confirmed breeding were derived from sightings of adults with attendant young. Some sites where this species was noted were hard to survey comprehensively, due to limitations placed on access and/or dense vegetation screening the water; breeding doubtless occurred in many such places but had to be regarded by the observers concerned as probable or even merely possible.

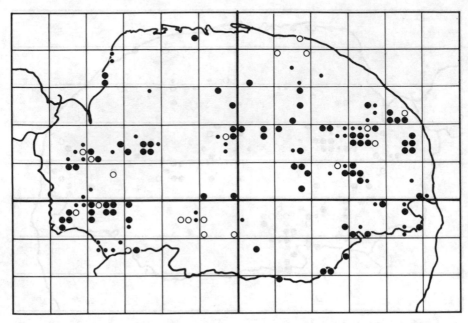

Great Crested Grebe

Podiceps cristatus

Tetrads recorded in:	149	(10%)
Possible breeding:	48	(32%)
Probable breeding:	20	(13%)
Confirmed breeding:	81	(54%)

A familiar breeding species on most of the larger inland sheets of water in the county, although rather scarce on the Breckland meres — these latter being more noted for their breeding Little Grebes. In addition, the Great Crested Grebe has extended its range over the last twenty years and has colonised the tidal Yare just below Norwich, rivers and channels in the Fens, and the pits by the shore of the Wash at Snettisham.

This handsome and fascinating bird was almost driven to extinction for the sake of its underpelts in Britain in the mid-19th century, and certain Broads were of significance among its few remaining refuges. Legislation came just in time to save it, and its numbers have generally tended to rise ever since. No full count of adults

was undertaken during the NBBS, although this total stood at 559 in 1975.

Breeding was easy to establish, for both nests and young could be spotted without difficulty from the banks of many of this bird's breeding stations. Certain waters from which confirmation was not forthcoming may only have held non-breeders or unmated birds, although some nests and young may have remained unmarked in particularly well-screened locations.

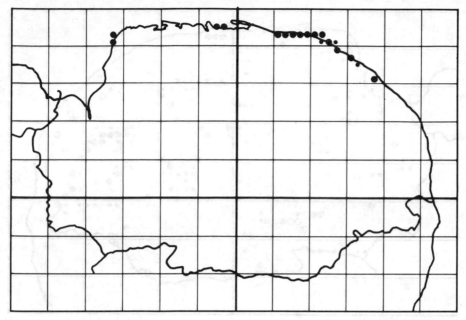

Fulmar

Fulmarus glacialis

Tetrads recorded in:	16	(1%)
Possible breeding:	3	(19%)
Probable breeding:	nil	
Confirmed breeding:	13	(81%)

This cliff-nesting species first prospected Norfolk sites in 1940, having been previously a winter visitor for the most part and one which only appeared in any numbers in stormy weather. Breeding was first proved in the boulder-clay cliffs at Weybourne in 1947, and suitable ledges and cavities in the extension of these eastwards to Happisburgh were progressively exploited thereafter. Breeding in the chalk and carrstone cliffs of Hunstanton commenced in 1964. A total of 247 sites were occupied in 1982.

Fulmars desert their nest-sites for the autumn, but frequent them at other times of the year. Virtually all the sites which are available to these birds are used to the full nowadays. Any further expansion of range in the county is hardly possible. In respect of the boulder-clay cliffs which they use, erosion may destroy a few nests each year; however, the profile of any section of cliff after a fall tends to contain an equal number of suitable sites as are lost in such an event.

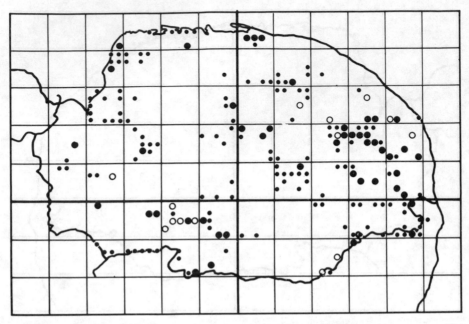

Grey Heron

Ardea cinerea

Tetrads recorded in:	203	(14%)
Possible breeding:	142	(70%)
Probable breeding:	14	(7%)
Confirmed breeding:	47	(23%)

Formerly one of the most familiar birds of Broadland, the Grey Heron also breeds in a wide variety of wetland habitats elsewhere in the county which contain suitable trees for it to nest in. Most of the principal heronries are checked annually, although while the NBBS was in progress a comprehensive count of nests within sites known to be occupied was only undertaken in 1983 — see the *Norfolk Bird Report* for that year, pp.364/5. This season was somewhat colder than the average, but not sufficiently so to have brought about a disturbing decline in the number of nests found. This was to be the case, however, for a total of 238 nests compared badly with the average of 336 occupied over the years from 1954 to 1969. This drop mostly related to the declining strength of Broadland heronries; this has been attributed to a variety of complex causes, one of which is likely to have been the lowering of the water table in many (sometimes ex-) grazing marshes since the 1960s.

Breeding was confirmed in 47 tetrads from 1980 to 1985, compared with 27 heronries found in the county in the single year 1983. However, it should be stated that not all traditional sites are occupied annually with some eventually being abandoned for good. Some isolated nests or small colonies may only be used for a single year. The nests become bulky, but their position cannot always be pinpointed where access is difficult or restricted. Some records of non-proven breeding related to such cases, although most of the possible ones concerned non-breeding birds or ones wandering far from their nests.

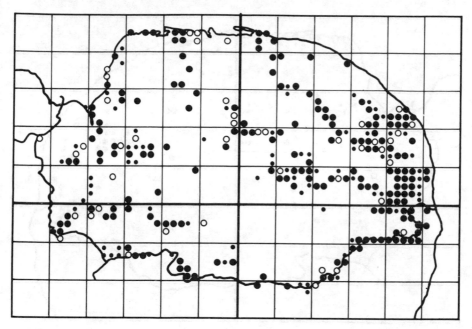

Mute Swan

Cygnus olor

Tetrads recorded in:	301	(21%)
Possible breeding:	76	(25%)
Probable breeding:	43	(14%)
Confirmed breeding:	182	(60%)

Data from NBBS workers was supplemented by that gathered in the 1983 Mute Swan Census, a project directed by the BTO and organised locally by Alec Bull and Moss Taylor. The above map should therefore represent a particularly accurate picture of this bird's distribution. Broadland is its natural stronghold, while it also nests along most favourable stretches of rivers upstream of the Broads. Relatively fewer birds breed in the west of the county, although the Great Ouse with the Ouse Washes, the Nar, the Wissey and the Little Ouse still had good numbers. Elsewhere, coastal lagoons, lakes, meres and gravel pits held most of the remaining breeding population.

In recent years, much publicity has been issued by conservationists concerning the fate of this species from such perils as pollution and disturbance by power craft (especially on the Broads), and anglers' lead weights and discarded line. It would be unkind to say that such dangers have been over-exaggerated. However, a growing awareness by public and private bodies, as well as by individuals, of the need to protect wildlife at risk in the last decade would seem to have reversed the decline in this bird's numbers which became apparent in Broadland in the early 1970s. Indeed, the 1983 Census showed a county-wide increase over the comparable count of 1978 in the numbers of breeding pairs, territorial pairs, and non-breeding birds, of 14%, 60% and 36% respectively. In 1983, 156 breeding pairs, 91 territorial pairs, and 916 non-breeding birds were counted. (For fuller details, refer to the *Norfolk Bird Report*, 1983, pp.340/1.)

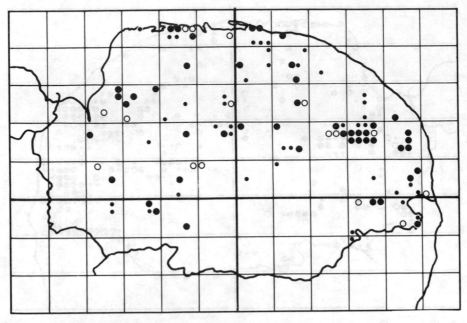

Greylag Goose

Anser anser

Tetrads recorded in:	110	(8%)
Possible breeding:	46	(42%)
Probable breeding:	17	(15%)
Confirmed breeding:	47	(43%)

	1968-1972		1980-1985
4	Possible breeding		12
1	Probable breeding		3
14	Confirmed breeding		25
19	10-km squares found in		40

In Britain, genuinely wild breeding Greylags are confined to Scotland north of the Great Glen and in the Outer Hebrides. Feral colonies were initially established elsewhere about 1930 and in the Norfolk Broads in particular in 1935. Smaller groups were subsequently placed at Cley and Holkham, but it is from all of these early flocks that the majority of the birds recorded by NBBS workers have both descended and spread from.

This bird has extended its range markedly in recent years, as can be shown by a comparison of its status in the BTO/IWC *Atlas* project of 1968-1972 and the NBBS of 1980-1985 — the figures given next relating to 10-km squares, *not* tetrads:

Returning to the tetrad as the recording unit, those where breeding was not confirmed had in most instances prospecting birds which would nest and establish thriving new colonies in time, save in cases of human disturbance or inhabitation. In parts of Broadland some consider Greylags to be a pest, partly due to their propensity for damaging reed-beds by grazing on the emerging shoots in spring.

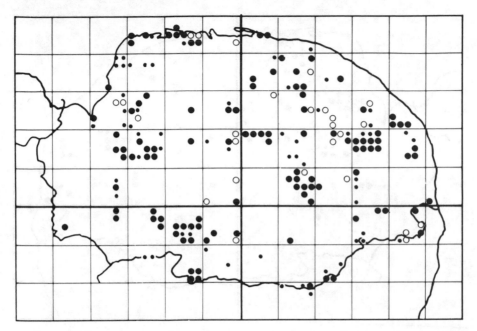

Canada Goose

Branta canadiensis

Tetrads recorded in:	201	(14%)
Possible breeding:	63	(31%)
Probable breeding:	26	(13%)
Confirmed breeding:	112	(56%)

Canada Geese are handsome birds, and, as for all large and widespread wildfowl, observers found breeding easy to prove through noting adults on their conspicuous nests or accompanied by their downy young.

The most numerous and widespread of the three species of geese breeding ferally in the county, it is likely that this was first introduced into certain parks with suitable lakes in the 18th century. Riviere, writing in 1930 (*Birds of Norfolk*), did not choose to discuss its status in detail; and, while it was shown to be well-represented in Norfolk on the BTO/IWC *Atlas* map which reflected 1968-1972 breeding records, it was observed that it had declined in numbers since 1965 in North Norfolk. The NBBS indicates that its range has become marginally more extensive since 1968-1972 although it is not possible to draw an exact parallel due to the non-coincidence of 10-km squares with the county boundary in the earlier project.

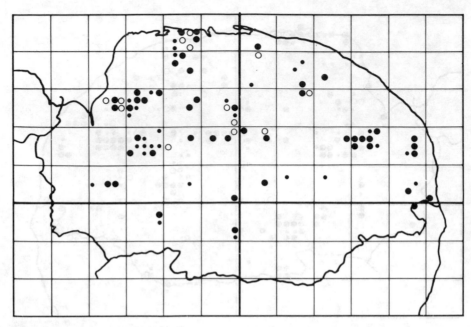

Egyptian Goose

Alopochen aegypiacus

Tetrads recorded in:	91	(6%)
Possible breeding:	30	(33%)
Probable breeding:	14	(15%)
Confirmed breeding:	47	(52%)

This 19th century introduction to four parks in the county: Holkham, Blickling, Gunton and Kimberley, still breeds freely in those localities. During the present century, a notable expansion of its range has occurred, and the birds breed in Broadland (in particular), about the upper Wensum, and in the valleys of the Nar and Babingley. Much of this expansion is owed to a dispersal from the early colonies, although fresh introductions (which are little documented) have also played a part in this.

The exploitation of new sites by this species would appear to have quickened in recent years in particular. This is borne out by a comparison of its status in the BTO/IWC *Atlas* project of 1968-1972 and the NBBS of 1980-1985 — the figures given next relating to 10-km squares, *not* tetrads:

1968-1972		1980-1985
1	Possible breeding	4
2	Probable breeding	1
10	Confirmed breeding	25
13	10-km squares found in	30

A continued expansion of this bird's range may be expected; many apparently suitable sites yet to be exploited remain, including gravel pits in the Waveney Valley as well as the Breckland meres.

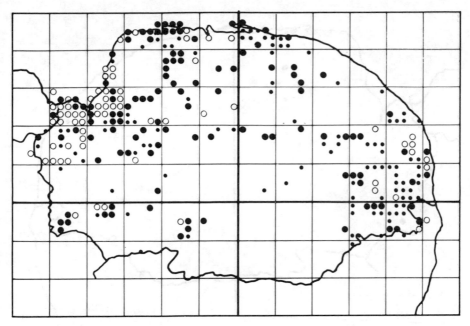

Shelduck

Tadorna tadorna

Tetrads recorded in:	286	(20%)
Possible breeding:	104	(36%)
Probable breeding:	67	(23%)
Confirmed breeding:	115	(40%)

This boldly patterned duck occurs as both a breeding and a non-breeding summer visitor, as well as a passage migrant and winter visitor. As a breeding bird, it has exhibited a steady increase in numbers with a parallel extension of its range throughout this present century. It was once restricted for the most part to coastal nesting sites, or at least to ones close to tidal water. These localities were often grazed by rabbits and their burrows utilised by Shelducks for nesting purposes. The decrease in the overall population of the rabbit since myxomatosis became endemic in the mid-1950s has seen Shelducks making far more use of such nest-sites as long grass, bramble patches and gorse clumps, straw bales and even buildings.

Early breeding sites in Norfolk were restricted to the north coast and the margins of the Wash, and it is from these parts that the Shelduck has most markedly spread inland during the last thirty years. A dispersal from Broadland, first colonised in the 1930s, has been less marked; indeed, the birds recorded about the upper reaches of both the Bure and the Wensum are more likely to have spread from the north coast population.

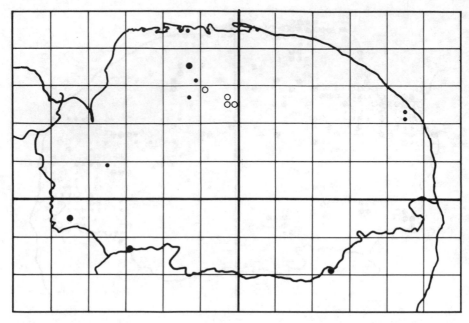

Wigeon

Anas penelope

Tetrads recorded in:	17	(1%)
Possible breeding:	8	(47%)
Probable breeding:	5	(29%)
Confirmed breeding:	4	(24%)

This bird is familiar to birdwatchers as a passage migrant and winter visitor, especially to the Fens, the Wash, the marshes of the north coast, and Broadland. The Wigeon is first known to have bred in Scotland (Sutherland) in 1834, and it first nested in England (Yorkshire) in 1897. The gradual southward spread was confidently expected to reach Norfolk, and the first breeding record was to come from Hickling in 1944. This far south, however, most records of breeding are believed, and in some instances known, to relate to birds which have escaped from wildfowl collections or to wild ones which were prevented from migrating in spring by injury.

Of the four records of proved breeding submitted by NBBS workers, those from South Creake and Shotford Pits are known to have concerned escapes — as are the probable breeding records from the upper Wensum. The pair which bred in the Ouse Washes may well have been genuinely wild, while the status of the pair which bred at Hockwold Fen is not known.

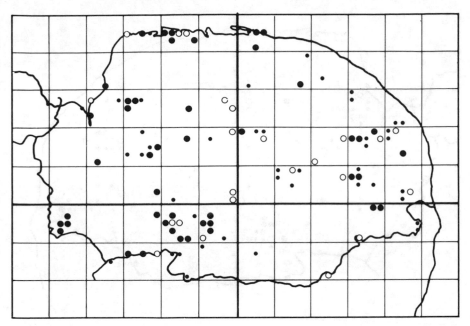

Gadwall

Anas strepera

Tetrads recorded in:	112	(8%)
Possible breeding:	43	(38%)
Probable breeding:	24	(21%)
Confirmed breeding:	45	(40%)

Once only known as a winter visitor, the descendants of a pinioned pair released on Narford Lake — tetrad TF71T, still a breeding location — about 1850 spread to the Breckland meres where they were to become established residents. Regular breeding spread to Broadland during the 1950s, in which decade the Ouse Washes were also colonised. By the time of the BTO/IWC *Atlas* project, 1968-1972, the north coast, the hinterland of King's Lynn and certain park lakes all had resident Gadwall.

Since 1972, a few sites which once held these birds have lost them, although a slightly larger number of new localities have been settled. Away from their main centres of population, only a few birds tended to gather in any given place — say, for instance, a stretch of the upper Wensum — and some broods of ducklings may have been missed by observers among the more numerous parties of Mallard.

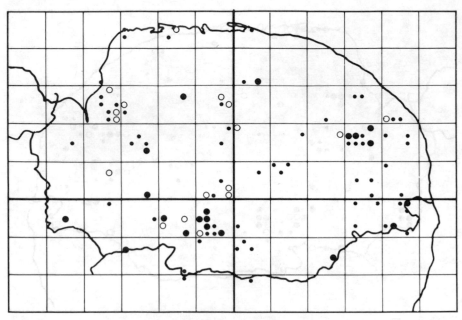

Teal

Anas crecca

Tetrads recorded in:	101	(7%)
Possible breeding:	63	(62%)
Probable breeding:	17	(17%)
Confirmed breeding:	21	(21%)

This duck is most prevalent as a passage migrant and winter visitor, and was once widespread as a breeding bird (Riviere, *History of the Birds of Norfolk*, 1930). Seago, writing in 1967 (*Birds of Norfolk*), observed that it was becoming scarcer as a breeding bird; and, while the BTO/IWC *Atlas* project of 1968-1972, with data plotted on a relatively coarse 10-km square grid, showed Teal breeding still in many parts of the county, the NBBS was to demonstrate a marked contraction of its range. Indeed, the above map, which compounds records received over the years 1980-1985, exaggerates the current status of the Teal as a resident bird.

Two centres of regular breeding remain: the Ranworth district of Broadland, and the

meres, marshes and pingos of Breckland. Elsewhere, save perhaps within the Ouse Washes, breeding records indicated on the map tended to be isolated occurrences. Some of the probable breeding records, especially those from the streams flowing out of the foot of the chalk escarpment to the east of King's Lynn, are likely to have constituted actual nesting; but most of the remaining non-proven records are likely to relate to birds which lingered well into spring before migrating. The absence of any confirmed breeding along the north coast, with its wealth of ideal (and wardened) habitat, provides the most cogent statement concerning the Teal's decline in Norfolk. The reasons for this decline would appear to be matters for conjecture.

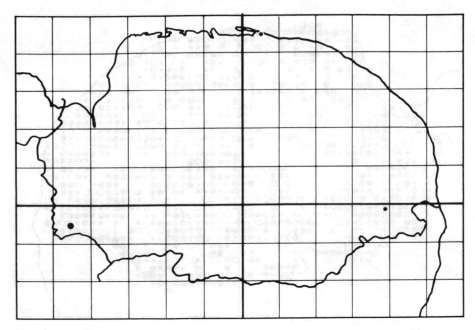

Pintail

Anas acuta

Tetrads recorded in:	4	(<1%)
Possible breeding:	3	(75%)
Probable breeding:	nil	
Confirmed breeding:	1	(25%)

Like the Wigeon, the Pintail colonised Britain as a breeding species in the 19th century; unlike the former bird it bred in southern England (Kent in 1910) before the first nest was discovered in Norfolk, on Roudham Heath in 1929. The Pintail has subsequently bred only very sparingly in the county, and only a single proven instance was submitted by a NBBS observer. This concerned the Ouse Washes, a locality where large numbers of these birds occur in winter. A peak of twenty pairs bred there in 1969 and 1970, a total which has not been approached since. (In dealing with records from the Ouse Washes, save for those submitted for the NBBS or when otherwise qualified, one should recall that the southern section of this sanctuary lies in Cambridgeshire.)

Three possible breeding records in suitable habitat were submitted; however, while breeding had occurred in one of the tetrads concerned: Cley between 1958 and 1960, there is little likelihood that the birds noted were other than late migrants or summering singletons which failed to find a mate.

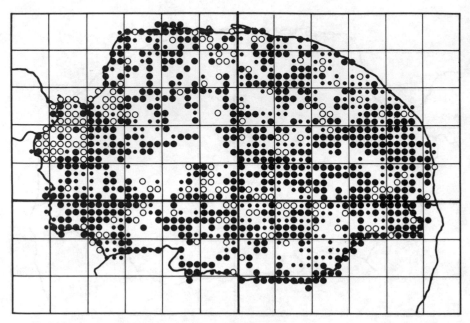

Mallard

Anas platyrhynchos

Tetrads recorded in:	1,026	(71%)
Possible breeding:	256	(25%)
Probable breeding:	159	(15%)
Confirmed breeding:	611	(60%)

The most common and widespread of the county's wildfowl, a bird which may even be taken for granted in some aquatic situations. These latter include village ponds, rivers in towns and parts of Broadland, where pure-bred Mallards which have become semi-tame are found in the company of others which have hybridized with ornamental and farmyard varieties. In order to give a true picture of the breeding range of the Mallard, observers were advised to ignore the presence of obvious hybrids; however, it is likely that a few records relating to such birds have appeared on the map.

This species occurs in both freshwater and brackish habitats; it is a particularly common breeding bird in Broadland and the valleys of the main rivers, while smaller streams, together with lakes and ponds, also produced records. Breeding was easily established during the long nesting season: nests were often located in readily visible spots, while newly fledged young attendant upon their parents are a familiar and pleasing sight. Even where breeding was not confirmed, it is likely to have occurred in most instances.

Areas without breeding Mallards included interfluves or watershed zones, heathland or former heathland (such as the pre-Enclosure Mousehold Heath, which extended from Norwich to Panxworth), dense plantations lacking ponds, and deeply drained parts of the Fens, especially in the Emneth district.

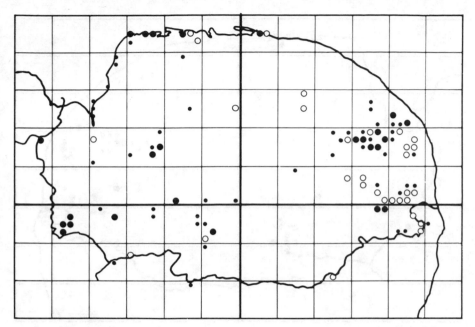

Shoveler

Anas clypeata

Tetrads recorded in:	104	(7%)
Possible breeding:	49	(47%)
Probable breeding:	30	(29%)
Confirmed breeding:	25	(24%)

This duck with its distinctive, spatulate bill is a locally common breeding bird, a passage migrant and a winter visitor. Its main centres of breeding are Broadland, the north coast, the Breckland meres and the Ouse Washes, as has been the case throughout this present century. While no marked change in its breeding numbers seems to have been commented upon by local ornithologists during the last few years, some sites away from its strongholds which held this species during the BTO/IWC *Atlas* project of 1968-1972 did not produce records for the NBBS.

It is not easy to prove breeding for this species unless ducklings are seen; and, while many records of probable breeding in Broadland were derived from observing patently territorial birds which surely nested in most instances, possible nesting occurrences away from the most favoured areas are for the most part likely to have concerned wandering, unmated individuals.

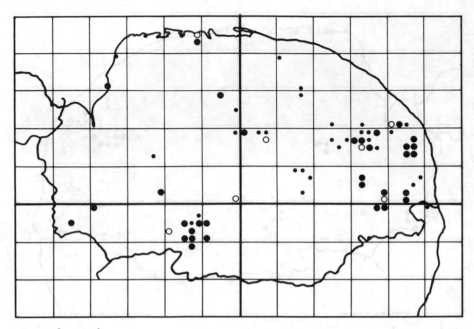

Pochard

Aythya ferina

Tetrads recorded in:	71	(5%)
Possible breeding:	32	(45%)
Probable breeding:	7	(10%)
Confirmed breeding:	32	(45%)

While it is far more numerous as a passage migrant and winter visitor, this species is known to have bred in the county since 1815 — at Scoulton Mere, where probable breeding was established during the NBBS. Away from Breckland, nesting occurred sporadically at Cley and in Broadland in the 1920s. The BTO/IWC *Atlas* survey of 1968-1972 indicated that it had become well established beyond Breckland, where the meres remain a stronghold, in particular in Broadland. The NBBS indicates no further expansion of consequence by 1985: a few sites abandoned since 1972 having been compensated for by breeding since being confirmed at Holkham and Pensthorpe, for instance.

Away from the Brecks and the Broads,

every tetrad which had confirmed breeding for this species also had breeding Tufted Duck, its close relation. The Pochard remains by far the least numerous breeding bird of the two, and has hardly begun to exploit the many flooded gravel pits which would appear to offer suitable habitat.

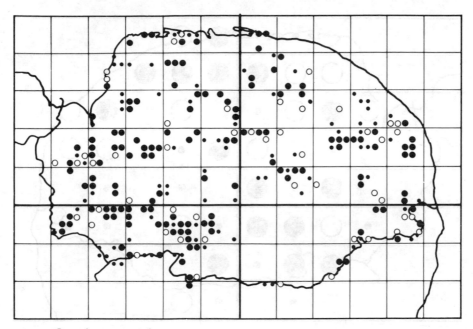

Tufted Duck

Aythya fuligula

Tetrads recorded in:	270	*(19%)*
Possible breeding:	88	(33%)
Probable breeding:	49	(18%)
Confirmed breeding:	133	(49%)

A passage migrant and winter visitor, this species has also been a breeding summer visitor since a nest was found at Merton in 1873 — some twenty-four years after Nottinghamshire provided the first British breeding record. From Merton, there was a spread to other Breckland waters which remain this bird's stronghold in the county. Sporadic breeding commenced in Broadland in 1912, but a major range expansion was only to follow in the train of the large-scale excavation of pits for gravel and sand from the 1940s. The NBBS has revealed that the Tufted Duck has by now exploited nearly all the suitable expanses of inland water and has begun to nest along sluggish stretches of rivers, in the Ouse Washes and by coastal lagoons.

This duck nests later in the spring than most waterfowl and, while almost one-half of the records submitted were of confirmed breeding, many of the remaining ones came from tetrads which were not visited after the time that nesting would normally have commenced. Some non-proven records would nevertheless have derived from sightings of prospecting or unmated birds.

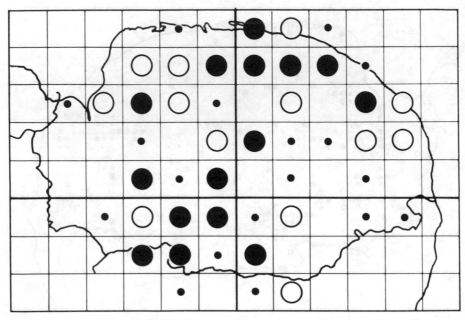

Sparrowhawk

Accipiter nisus

Tetrads recorded in:	126	(9%)
Possible breeding:	80	(63%)
Probable breeding:	24	(19%)
Confirmed breeding:	22	(18%)

Within each 10-km square, with one exception, the highest category of record(s) received from the tetrads therein has been plotted centrally. The exception is that the only record of confirmed breeding in a 10-km square in the TG 100-km square has not been plotted at the request of the observer concerned. Naturalists will appreciate the cautious approach to this species in the *Norfolk Bird Atlas*.

This splendid hawk, once a widespread breeding resident, was almost reduced to its subsidiary categorisations of passage migrant and winter visitor in the late 1950s and early 1960s, due to its ingestion of toxic chemicals. A small number continued to nest in Breckland, Broadland and in the vicinity of the north coast, however.

Despite the legal protection which was accorded this species in 1963, and the restrictions which were placed upon the use of toxic chemicals in agriculture, its recovery in the county has been somewhat slow. Records submitted during the NBBS at least give rise to a belief that this recovery may be gathering pace in certain areas.

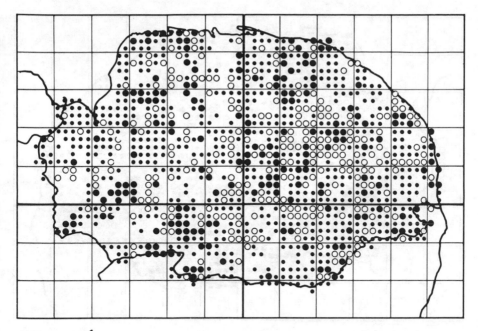

Kestrel

Falco tinnunculus

Tetrads recorded in:	1,054	(72%)
Possible breeding:	602	(57%)
Probable breeding:	263	(24%)
Confirmed breeding:	189	(18%)

Whether or not it is performing its distinctive hovering flight, this bird is a familiar sight throughout the larger part of the county and is, furthermore, the most common raptor. Its population, which fell to a low level in the early 1960s as a consequence of the largely unrestricted use of pesticides on crops, has since risen thanks to prohibitions or restrictions in respect of such chemical dressings. The Kestrel is widespread in farmland with plenty of trees, in woodland, and in Broadland and Breckland. It mostly nests in holes in trees, but will sometimes utilise old nests of Carrion Crows and Magpies. It will also exploit buildings and even structures such as pylons in built-up areas and in open marshland. NBBS workers found breeding pairs in Great Yarmouth, although none was proved to breed in inner Norwich during this period.

Kestrel which were seen by observers only briefly were generally accorded possible breeding status. Even during the height of the breeding season, this bird will often search for food well beyond the confines of any tetrad it might be nesting in so it is likely that only a limited number of such records related to breeding pairs. Bearing this in mind, this species is seen to be scarce or absent in such open Fens as Stow Bardolph, Upwell and Methwold, and in intensively farmed districts with a paucity of woodland such as the country between Hindringham and Wells-next-the-Sea in the north, and that between the Lophams and Tibenham in the south.

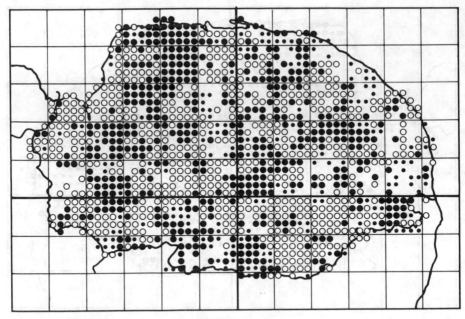

Red-legged Partridge

Alectoris rufa

Tetrads recorded in:	1,307	(90%)
Possible breeding:	173	(13%)
Probable breeding:	667	(51%)
Confirmed breeding:	467	(36%)

This introduced species was first recorded in Norfolk in 1790, but it is not believed to have had a self-sustaining population here until the early 19th century. It adapted well to the wide expanses of country with light or calcareous soils, while the low rainfall (relatively speaking) which obtains here has also been to its liking. By the end of the 1960s, it had become apparent to Norfolk ornithologists that its population had come to exceed that of the native Grey Partridge.

This bird was found in 90% of the tetrads, the third most widespread non-passerine species (after the Woodpigeon and the Pheasant). Whereas the Grey Partridge was once prevalent in all cultivated districts, the NBBS has revealed that throughout many tracts of country the Red-legged was

the only species of partridge to be found. Given its sedentary nature, most records of the Red-legged Partridge which fell short of confirmed breeding are likely to have related to actual nesting.

The two partridge species co-exist quite happily: the high number of tetrads with confirmed breeding for both in the traditional partridge country of North-west Norfolk point to this.

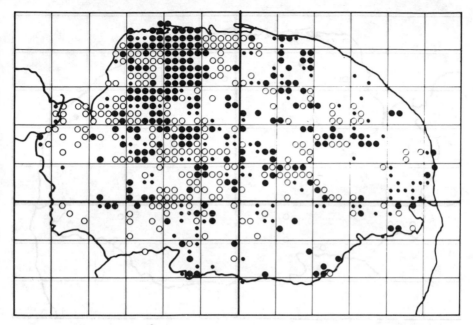

Grey Partridge

Perdix perdix

Tetrads recorded in:	545	*(37%)*
Possible breeding:	110	(20%)
Probable breeding:	215	(39%)
Confirmed breeding:	220	(40%)

The above map graphically illustrates the well-known decline, particularly marked in the last decade, of this once familiar and widespread denizen of virtually all cultivated land in the county. Despite its having been independently surveyed by four NBBS workers, 10-km square TG23 in North-east Norfolk which has a high percentage of land eminently suited to this bird's requirements did not produce a single record. Cool and wet springs in recent years, together with changes in agricultural methods, have been blamed for the decline, although other and perhaps subtler factors may also have been at play.

The Grey Partridge is still widespread and even common in the north-west of the county, where there has been a tradition of game conservation on a large scale since at least as far back as the early 18th century. In some parts of Norfolk, this species' numbers are actually kept up by landowners having birds artificially reared then subjected to no or to only limited shooting in season.

While this species is sedentary, in tetrads where it has occurred in isolation it would not be safe to consider records which fell short of confirmed breeding as necessarily constituting actual nesting.

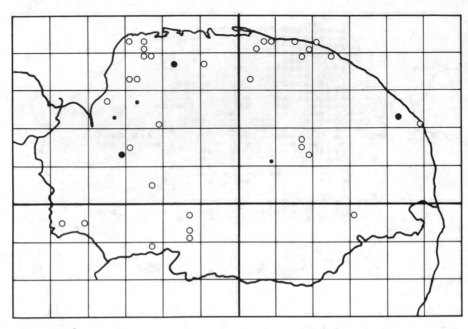

Quail

Coturnix coturnix

Tetrads recorded in:	38	(3%)
Possible breeding:	3	(8%)
Probable breeding:	33	(87%)
Confirmed breeding:	2	(5%)

One record of probable breeding in the TF61 10-km square has not been mapped at the request of the observer concerned.

A very scarce summer visitor, mostly located through hearing its call in cornfields — especially on the chalk of North-west Norfolk — and in hayfields and the drier margins of marshes. As it tends to be seen only when accidentally flushed, some NBBS workers who were unfamiliar with its call may have missed a few instances of its occurence. While such a scarce bird might be expected to remain unmated in some instances, it is to be hoped that rather more than the two instances of confirmed breeding indicated above actually occurred over the 1980-1985 period.

This species is protected in Great Britain at all times by special penalties under Schedule 1, Part I of the Wildlife and Countryside Act, 1981.

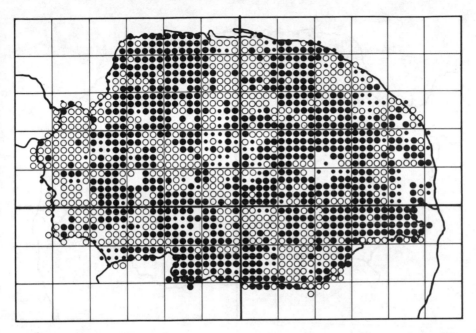

Pheasant

Phasianus colchicus

Tetrads recorded in:	*1,349*	*(93%)*
Possible breeding:	115	(9%)
Probable breeding:	494	(37%)
Confirmed breeding:	740	(55%)

Even before one spots this colourful and distinctive component of the Norfolk countryside, one may well hear the unmistakable kokking call of the male indicating its presence. This species is believed to have been introduced by the Normans about the time of Domesday (1086), but despite its being subject to large-scale management it is usually regarded as a natural feature of our avifauna. Many of the extensive blocks of land in which this bird was proved to breed in every tetrad contain estates where it is intensively reared for game; nevertheless, while observers were not expected to go out of their way to ignore either adult or young Pheasant which *may* have been bred in captivity, such tetrads should have held at least some birds which would have

raised broods without any human intervention.

Strutting, displaying males, or birds entering or leaving likely nest sites in banks and verges, gave rise to most of the probable breeding records. Many of these originated from tetrads where there was little or no intensive management, which suggests that the Pheasant would still be widespread but not abundant without the assistance of gamekeepers.

After the Woodpigeon, this was found to be the most widespread non-passerine bird; one that was for the most part only absent from Halvergate Levels, exposed coastal tetrads, and the heavily built-up areas of Norwich and Great Yarmouth.

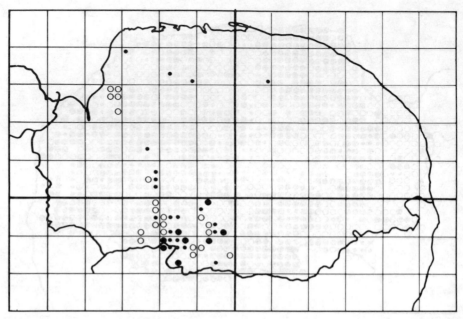

Golden Pheasant

Chrysolophus pictus

Tetrads recorded in:	50	(3%)
Possible breeding:	20	(40%)
Probable breeding:	22	(44%)
Confirmed breeding:	8	(16%)

A resident species, introduced to certain Breckland estates in the late 1890s and probably subsequently. This area has remained its stronghold, both in respect of Norfolk and nationally. A number of records from the Sandringham district concern the descendants of a separate introduction in or about 1967. The scatter of records of possible breeding from other localities in the north of the county are likely to relate to escapes from collections.

Considering that the male is such a large, gaudy bird, it might surprise those birdwatchers unfamiliar with it that it is for the most part difficult to observe. It likes to skulk in its favoured resorts of plantations, shelter-belts and thickets, and when it does venture out into the open it will dash for cover upon the slightest disturbance. All the colonies within Breckland and about Sandringham would appear to be self-supporting, so it follows that many of the records of this bird which fell short of confirmed breeding would actually have related to this.

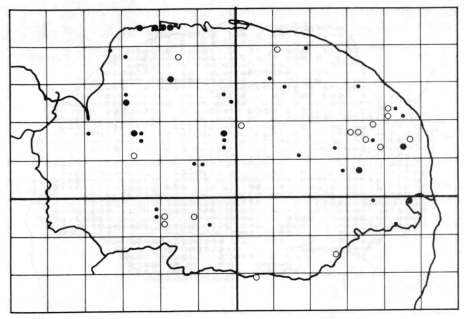

Water Rail

Rallus aquaticus

Tetrads recorded in:	55	(4%)
Possible breeding:	27	(49%)
Probable breeding:	17	(31%)
Confirmed breeding:	11	(20%)

This species was considered by Riviere (*History of the Birds of Norfolk*) in 1930 to be a common although somewhat local breeding bird, but it had become much scarcer by 1967 when Seago wrote *Birds of Norfolk*. This decline has since all but stalled, given a comparison with the data collected during the BTO/IWC *Atlas* project of 1968-1972 and the NBBS of 1980-1985.

The Water Rail is not an easy bird to observe, even when it has revealed its presence by its peculiar grunting and squealing calls. Its slender body is well suited to facilitating its passage through its preferred habitat of dense vegetation in Broadland, coastal reed beds, and marshes and swamps elsewhere. The most regular instances of confirmed breeding during the NBBS came from within or close to wardened reserves, especially Strumpshaw Fen and the stretch of coastal marsh between Thornham and Burnham Norton.

Breeding was mostly confirmed through seeing adults with downy young by open water at the edge of thick cover. Given this species' elusiveness, many records of probable and even possible breeding from suitable habitat in May and June (as shown above) should have related to actual nesting.

Moorhen

Gallinula chloropus

Tetrads recorded in:	1,198	(82%)
Possible breeding:	92	(7%)
Probable breeding:	101	(8%)
Confirmed breeding:	1,005	(84%)

This is by far the most common and widespread breeding bird associated with wetlands including habitats which are merely damp. Its range is not dissimilar to that of the Mallard but extends into more marginal localities. Breeding Moorhens were found, for instance, in the smallest ponds, wet ditches and marl-pits, damp patches in fields and moist meadowland, all of which sites either lacked or had but an occasional nesting Mallard.

A few Moorhens nested close to the Yare in Great Yarmouth town, but most tended to avoid water with strong tides and, to some extent, the brackish lagoons about Wells-next-the-Sea and to the seaward face of Scolt Head, where Mallards *were* found. Moorhens were also scarce on Terrington Marsh, for reasons which are unclear.

Breeding was easy to prove for this species, either through locating the nest or by spotting the newly hatched chicks in the company of their parents. Some family parties were even noted on roadside pits from the upper deck of buses.

36

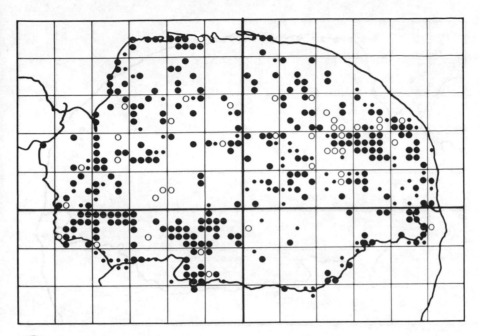

Coot

Fulica atra

Tetrads recorded in:	387	(27%)
Possible breeding:	87	(22%)
Probable breeding:	39	(10%)
Confirmed breeding:	261	(67%)

A less common and widespread breeding bird than its relation, the Moorhen, this is nevertheless a familiar component of the county's wetland avifauna. Coots range further afield in winter, partly to avoid the icing which tends to affect inland waters, but during spring and summer they are easily noted on Broads and lakes, large ponds, and about Fenland drains and many coastal lagoons.

It is unlikely that this distinctive bird was missed by observers; there are, in addition, some indications that it has tended to increase in numbers in recent years and to exploit new waters — the latter point is borne out by the fact that fresh breeding sites were discovered in the first post-NBBS season (1986) which are known not to have been occupied previously.

Some of the records of possible and probable breeding came from waters which observers could only visit once or which they could not check thoroughly due to difficulty of access. Given suitable habitat, breeding should have occurred in most such cases.

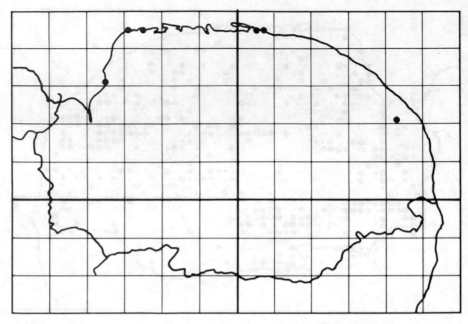

Avocet

Recurvirostra avosetta

Tetrads recorded in: 6   (<1%)
Possible breeding: nil
Probable breeding: nil
Confirmed breeding: 6   (100%)

A traditional breeding bird of the marshy lagoons and gently shelving muddy banks of the north coast and Broadland, this population died out about 1824. The Avocet was then to remain for long as a scarce passage migrant and, to a lesser extent, as an occasional visitor at other times. Attempted breeding at Salthouse in 1941 was followed six years later by the establishment of nesting colonies on the Suffolk coast which remain to this day. Norfolk ornithologists not unnaturally looked forward to the day when this bird would once again breed here regularly, a hope fostered by a further attempt which was made near King's Lynn in 1970. Success was eventually forthcoming at Cley in 1977, in which year a nest near Snettisham was unfor-

tunately trampled by cattle.

From the establishment of the Cley colony in 1977, successful nesting has occurred in each subsequent season. A pair was to breed at nearby Salthouse in 1981, and breeding has since occurred at two other north coast localities, as well as at Hickling and Snettisham. Over seventy chicks were raised in 1983.

All Avocet colonies which have formed in recent years and those which have been used on occasions have enjoyed the protective mantle of the wardened reserve. Readers are reminded that this species is protected in Great Britain at all times by special penalties under Schedule 1, Part I of the Wildlife and Countryside Act, 1981.

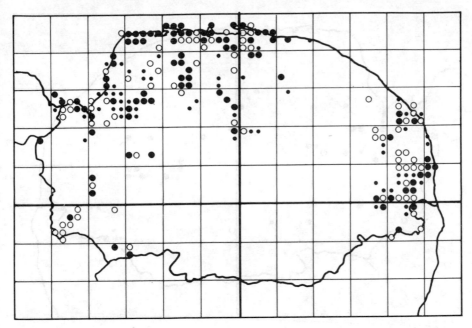

Oystercatcher

Haematopus ostralegus

Tetrads recorded in:	217	(15%)
Possible breeding:	55	(25%)
Probable breeding:	75	(35%)
Confirmed breeding:	87	(40%)

Until about 1940, the Oystercatcher was restricted as a breeding bird to coastal habitats — mostly shingle and salt-marsh. Over the next three decades a gradual spread into Broadland and Fenland levels and grazing marshes, as well as coastal fields, became apparent. Since the end of the BTO/IWC *Atlas* project in 1972, this bird has taken to nest even more extensively in the Broads and Fens and, in addition, on open pasture and arable land — especially stony fields — well inland in North-west Norfolk. That this feature was widely noted by NBBS workers may be seen on the above map. Of especial significance is the apparent 'leap' from the Burn Valley and its flanking agricultural land to further suitable habitat in the Wensum Valley below Fakenham.

Inland breeding is widespread throughout Scotland and over a large part of North-west England, and might reasonably be expected on current trends to gather impetus in Norfolk. Given the distinctive appearance of this bird, logging such progress can be undertaken by newcomers to birdwatching as well as by old hands.

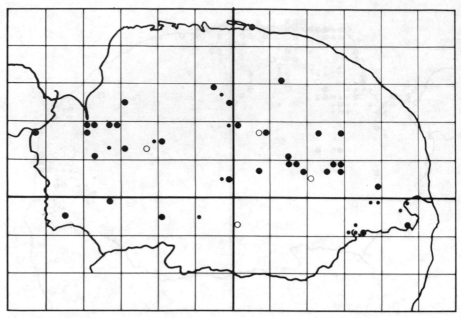

Little Ringed Plover

Charadrius dubius

Tetrads recorded in:	51	(4%)
Possible breeding:	13	(25%)
Probable breeding:	4	(8%)
Confirmed breeding:	34	(67%)

A passage migrant, first recorded in 1949, and a summer visitor which is first known to have bred in the county in 1960 — twenty-two years after the first British occurrence in Hertfordshire. While this remains a somewhat local breeding bird, numbers have gradually increased and thirty-four pairs summered in 1984. Most Little Ringed Plovers have bred at gravel pits, including those which are still being worked. Other localities favoured include beet factory settling ponds, floodwater on riverside meadows and inland fields, the former Wisbech Sewage Farm and even a factory roof at King's Lynn. Sadly, the three young which were hatched at the latter site in 1984 perished in storms when five days old. Only one near-coastal site was noted during the NBBS, at Cley (tetrad TG04M). There have been instances of Little Ringed Plovers being usurped from sites which they have chosen by Ringed Plovers.

As many of the sites used by this bird are predictable, it is not surprising that it was proved to breed in two-thirds of the tetrads in which it was recorded. Most of the remaining records are likely to have concerned transient or unmated individuals.

It must be stated that this species is protected at all times in Great Britain by special penalties under Schedule 1, Part I of the Wildlife and Countryside Act, 1981.

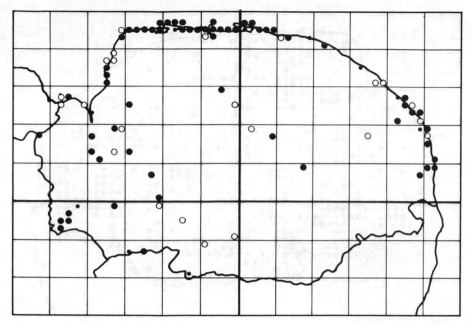

Ringed Plover

Charadrius hiaticula

Tetrads recorded in:	96	(7%)
Possible breeding:	11	(11%)
Probable breeding:	24	(25%)
Confirmed breeding:	61	(64%)

A locally common breeding bird, an abundant passage migrant and also a winter visitor. Around the coast of The Wash, and along the north coast as far east as Salthouse, it has always been recorded as a regular breeder. The population along the dune-backed beaches in the east has also thrived since a near-desertion of that area during the late 19th and early 20th centuries. Breeding in Breckland, first noted in 1836, had declined since the majority of the heaths frequented were planted with conifers from the 1920s. Seago, writing in 1967 (*Birds of Norfolk*), observed that most of the Ringed Plovers remaining in the Brecks had taken to nesting in arable fields; but despite this switch of habitat, the NBBS has registered a further decline there since the

BTO/IWC *Atlas* fieldwork of 1968-1972.

Coastal and Breckland Ringed Plovers have thus shown changes in their breeding ranges; but, more dramatically, this bird has come to exploit sites such as gravel pits, beet factory settling ponds, and the Ouse Washes during the last two to three decades. This trend has perhaps been somewhat obscured by the greater interest shown in the Little Ringed Plovers which have exploited similar, and often the same, sites over the same period.

In a special census of breeding Ringed Plovers undertaken in 1984, 529 pairs were located. This renders Norfolk of national significance for this species (see *Norfolk Bird Report*, 1984, p.102).

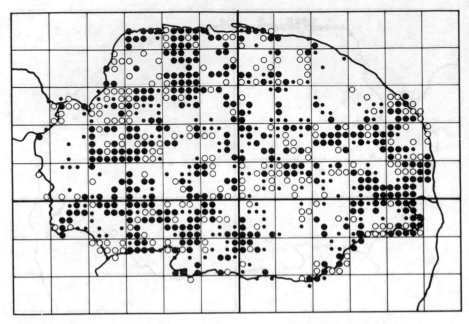

Lapwing

Vanellus vanellus

Tetrads recorded in:	772	(53%)
Possible breeding:	184	(24%)
Probable breeding:	219	(28%)
Confirmed breeding:	369	(48%)

A widespread breeding bird, as well as an abundant passage migrant and winter visitor. This, the most familiar of all waders, has declined as a breeding species during the course of the present century: a decline particularly occasioned by the draining of wetland meadows and the mechanization of agricultural procedures. Nevertheless, the NBBS has shown that it remains well established and, given the increased concern which now obtains throughout society for conservation, there are grounds for believing that its decline has been halted in many districts.

Seeing sitting birds in open fields, adults performing distraction displays, and downy young with their parents, were the usual instances of how breeding was proved. This

was the case in almost one-half of the records submitted; but sighting displaying birds in suitable nesting habitat, which constituted most of the instances of probable breeding, should also have related to such success.

This conspicuous bird could hardly have been overlooked, so the map must provide an excellent indication of its range. The lack of breeding Lapwings in parts of North-east and South Norfolk was commented upon by a number of observers.

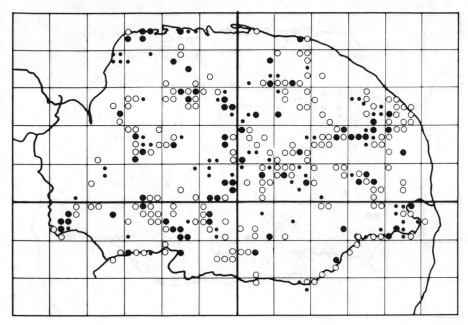

Snipe

Gallinago gallinago

Tetrads recorded in:	*325*	*(22%)*
Possible breeding:	71	(22%)
Probable breeding:	181	(56%)
Confirmed breeding:	73	(22%)

While this species is most abundant as a passage migrant and winter visitor, Norfolk wetlands have always attracted a high breeding population. This is a bird which is susceptible to habitat loss, in particular through the drainage of the once widespread wet meadow with its tussock-type vegetation. Such drainage has mostly served the cause of more efficient agricultural practices, although it has also been undertaken in connection with building development and by-pass construction; it has caused a considerable reduction in the numbers of breeding Snipe since the Second World War. Nevertheless, the county still retains much suitable habitat for this bird; and, in the joint BTO/RSPB survey of the breeding waders of wet meadows in England and Wales of 1982, 500 drumming birds — representing probable breeding pairs — were located in Norfolk, 23% of the total for England and Wales. (See *Norfolk Bird Report* 1982, pp.196-201.)

The above map shows a close correlation between the Snipe's range and the major river systems, inclusive of the Ouse Washes and much of Broadland. While a few records were submitted from the North Norfolk salt-marshes, this habitat is of minor importance for this species. It will be observed that the larger part of the Fens, as well as Broadland levels, had very few breeding season records, for such areas are too dry nowadays for the Snipe's liking.

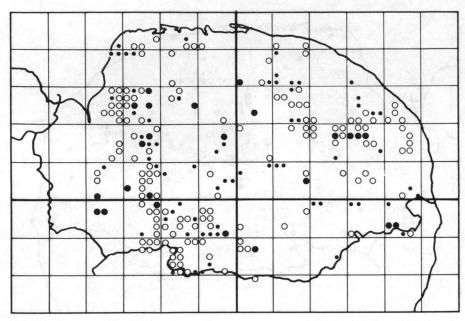

Woodcock

Scolopax rusticola

Tetrads recorded in:	233	(16%)
Possible breeding:	67	(29%)
Probable breeding:	141	(61%)
Confirmed breeding:	25	(11%)

A widespread and locally common breeding bird within its preferred habitat of deciduous and mixed woodland and young coniferous plantations, especially where there is a layer of bracken and ready access to damp areas for feeding purposes. It is considered that this species has in fact increased for the most part in recent years. As an exception, disappointingly few records came from the well-wooded Cromer-Holt ridge which was once a favoured district. This bird's major stronghold is Breckland, together with the heavily timbered band of country extending north-north-westwards from there to Sandringham. It is also well represented in northern Broadland, and in the somewhat discontinuous chain of woodland from Horsford north-west to Briston.

It is not easy to prove breeding for this crepuscular species; however, many of the instances of probable breeding (which were mostly gathered through seeing displaying birds) ought to relate to nesting. Many of the possible breeding records submitted are likely to have concerned lingering winter visitors.

44

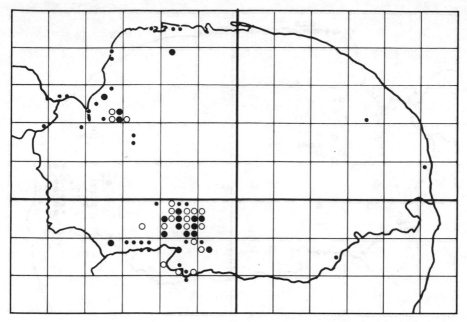

Curlew

Numenius arquata

Tetrads recorded in:	69	*(5%)*
Possible breeding:	33	(48%)
Probable breeding:	19	(28%)
Confirmed breeding:	17	(25%)

A somewhat scarce and local summer visitor, far more abundant as a passage migrant and winter visitor. Breeding was first noted in the two main areas in which it was to establish itself: the north-eastern hinterland of King's Lynn and Breckland, in 1889 and 1949 respectively. The latter area has become the more significant, and in holding about twenty breeding pairs annually is this species' most important stronghold in the whole of East Anglia and South-east England. A pair which nested in the peat Fens at Feltwell Anchor (tetrad TL68D) may have been overflow stock from Breckland; another pair which nested on a chalky, stony field at North Creake (TF83B) are more likely to have ventured from birds passing along the north coast than from those frequenting the heathland to the north-east of King's Lynn.

Many breeding Curlews are afforded incidental protection within the Battle Area of northern Breckland. Elsewhere, it is essential that human disturbance is kept to an absolute minimum to allow this superb wader to thrive; about Roydon Common in particular. Heath fires, including one in 1981 during the NBBS, have destroyed more than one clutch.

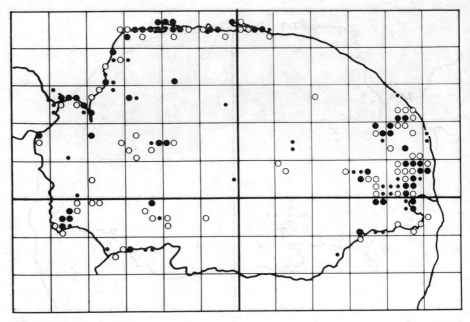

Redshank

Tringa totanus

Tetrads recorded in:	167	*(11%)*
Possible breeding:	41	(25%)
Probable breeding:	70	(42%)
Confirmed breeding:	56	(34%)

By far the largest numbers of Redshank occur as passage migrants and winter visitors, but this bird also remains a well-represented breeding species in the major wetland complexes of the county. All the same, one has to recall that when Riviere wrote his *History of the Birds of Norfolk* in 1930, this was a common breeding bird in river valleys well inland, as well as by the meres of Breckland; the use of many such sites would appear to have ceased since the early 1970s, judging from the above map compared with that printed in the BTO/IWC *Atlas.* Certain gravel pits might be considered to provide suitable nesting habitat, but no instance of confirmed breeding from such sites proper was submitted during the NBBS.

The BTO and the RSPB jointly organised a national survey of the breeding waders of wet meadows in England and Wales in 1982; some 388 pairs of Redshank were located in Norfolk, but it must be emphasized that this project did not encompass the chain of saltmarsh around the coastline from The Wash to Salthouse which is as important in respect of this bird's breeding status here as Broadland.

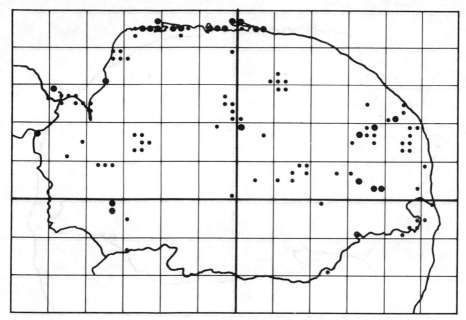

Black-headed Gull

Tetrads recorded in:	109	(7%)
Possible breeding:	84	(77%)
Probable breeding:	nil	
Confirmed breeding:	25	(23%)

The most widespread and familiar gull in the county, be it as a summer visitor, a passage migrant or a winter visitor. Nowadays most breeding colonies are coastal or in Broadland, but reference might be made here to the famous gullery at Scoulton Mere just beyond the north-east tip of Breckland which was first recorded in the 17th century and which survived until 1957. Coastal sites included dunes, saltings and shingle, as well as the grassy trial bund in The Wash (TF52A). Broadland sites included flooded marshland, as at How Hill, the settling ponds at Cantley Beet Factory (which can be seen from passing trains), and Alderfen, Hoveton Little and Rockland Broads. Fenland sites were restricted to Wisbech Sewage Farm and Wissington Beet Factory — a colony which fell within two tetrads. Breeding was also established at Swanton Morley Gravel Pits in the upper Wensum Valley.

No records of probable breeding were submitted by NBBS workers, although a high number of sightings were considered to constitute valid possible nesting records. Many of these concerned valley sites well inland and might be disregarded, although a few of these instances in Broadland and the Fens might have related to a pair or small colony which did eventually stay to breed.

During the NBBS, the number of birds which are known to have bred ranged between 1,500 and 3,300; flooding, including tidal inundations, destroying nests or inhibiting nesting in some seasons.

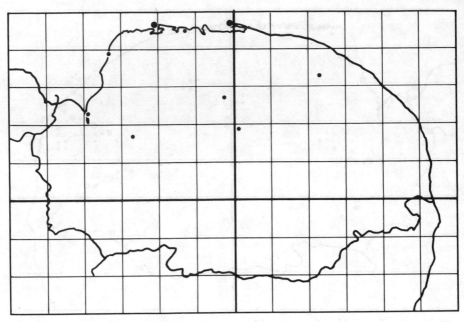

Common Gull

Larus canus

Tetrads recorded in:	9	(<1%)
Possible breeding:	7	(78%)
Probable breeding:	nil	
Confirmed breeding:	2	(22%)

Apart from the Black-headed Gull, no other species of gull breeds widely in Norfolk, nor, for that matter, between the Thames and the Humber. The Common Gull in particular is not what its name suggests, the most common gull either in this county or nationally. Nevertheless, it is still an abundant winter visitor and passage migrant, as well as a common non-breeding summer visitor (although it is scarce inland then). In addition, a few pairs breed intermittently.

NBBS workers reported instances of successful breeding at the western extremities of both Scolt Head and Blakeney Point. These sites were close to the only two sites utilised during the BTO/IWC *Atlas* survey period of 1968-1972; indeed Blakeney Point was where this species first bred successfully in the county in 1966. Observers submitted seven records of possible breeding; those from inland tetrads are virtually certain to have related to wandering non-breeders.

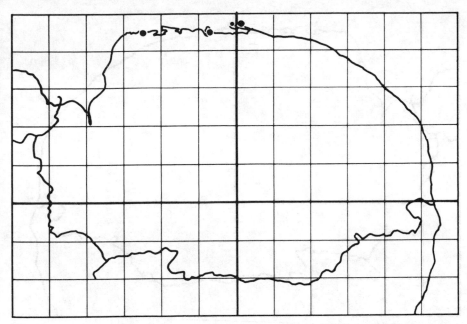

Lesser Black-backed Gull

Larus fuscus

Tetrads recorded in:	4	(<1%)
Possible breeding:	1	(25%)
Probable breeding:	nil	
Confirmed breeding:	3	(75%)

This species is best known as a passage migrant and non-breeding summer visitor, although it does occur in very small numbers in winter. Successful breeding occurred for the first time in the county at Blakeney Point in 1978, when a single chick was reared. This locality has been used in most subsequent years with up to eight pairs having nested. From 1981, Titchwell has provided a haven for a small colony, while another was established on the Wells/Warham Salt Marshes in 1984.

One further instance of possible breeding was submitted from the far tip of Blakeney Point; however, two sites where breeding was attempted but where it is known that it was not successful are not mapped (Scolt Head and Hickling Broad). All the same the signs are that this handsome gull will increasingly exploit suitable nesting habitat in the county.

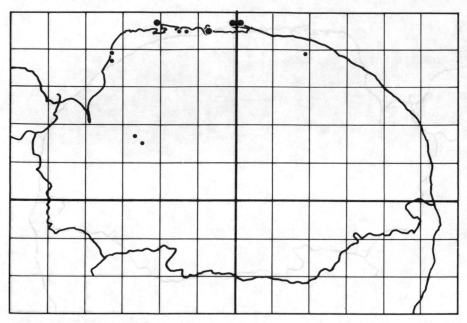

Herring Gull

Larus argentatus

Tetrads recorded in:	11	(<1%)
Possible breeding:	7	(64%)
Probable breeding:	nil	
Confirmed breeding:	4	(36%)

Like the closely related Lesser Black-backed Gull, this is a common passage migrant and non-breeding summer visitor; conversely, it is even more widespread in the winter months. Breeding was first established at Blakeney Point in 1972, the final year of the BTO/IWC *Atlas* project. This site has been used in most subsequent years, with between fifteen and twenty pairs having bred in 1985 — the dividing line between tetrads TF94J and TG04F passing through the colony, so both are shown with confirmed breeding on the map. Breeding also commenced at Scolt Head and on the Wells/Warham Salt Marshes in 1984.

Coastal sites from which NBBS observers submitted possible breeding records may well be colonized in due course; such records from inland localities almost certainly relate to wandering, scavenging birds. An unsuccessful breeding attempt in 1981 at Cantley Beet Factory is not mapped. To conclude, the Herring Gull like the Lesser Black-backed Gull seems to be in the early stages of a marked expansion of its breeding range which specifically concerns Norfolk.

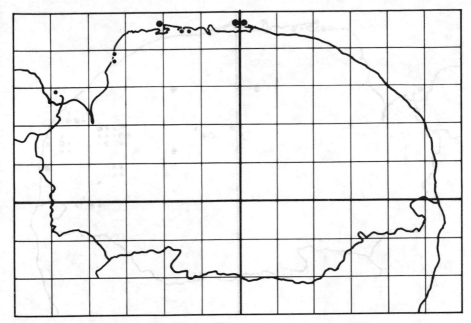

Sandwich Tern

Sterna sandvicensis

Tetrads recorded in:	11	*(<1%)*
Possible breeding:	7	(64%)
Probable breeding:	1	(9%)
Confirmed breeding:	3	(27%)

This summer visitor is first known to have bred in the county at Blakeney Point in 1920. It is Norfolk's most numerous breeding tern, despite the fact that it is only known to have bred in two localities — one spread into two tetrads during the NBBS. Proved breeding has, with one exception, always been restricted to the sand and shingle beaches of the north coast; it did occur in many seasons from 1947 to 1976 on Scroby Sands off Great Yarmouth, but this site subsequently disappeared. (As Scroby became submerged prior to the commencement of the NBBS, it is not shown on the maps in this book.)

During the NBBS, the approximate numbers of breeding Sandwich Terns at the two well-known colonies of Blakeney Point and Scolt Head amounted to between 3,500 and 4,200. The relative proportion of birds at each colony varied from year to year, Scolt having been the smaller of the two save in 1985. Past breeding sites, at Stiffkey and Salthouse, were not used, but records of possible and (in one instance, probable) breeding from The Wash and the Burnham Overy areas may relate to potential sites being prospected.

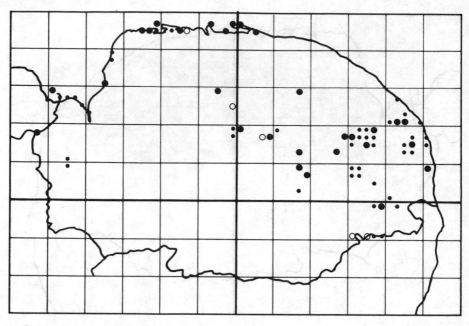

Common Tern

Sterna hirundo

Tetrads recorded in:	77	(5%)
Possible breeding:	42	(55%)
Probable breeding:	6	(8%)
Confirmed breeding:	29	(38%)

The most widespread nesting tern and, indeed, proved to breed in more tetrads than any other representative of the *Laridae*. Common Terns are, however, less numerous than Sandwich Terns.

A peak breeding population of 4,400 pairs was reached in 1938; about 1,500 pairs were recorded in 1980 but no more than 1,000 in subsequent seasons — inclement weather conditions and high spring tides having been partly to blame.

Many North Coast colonies, associated with shingle beaches, are traditional; the Broads were first colonised in 1949. Rafts, first used in Broadland to entice Common Terns, have since encouraged them to nest at gravel pits.

Prospecting birds were generally accorded possible breeding status; those seen in locations where nesting is hardly likely to occur, such as the Wensum in central Norwich, were not entered upon NBBS cards.

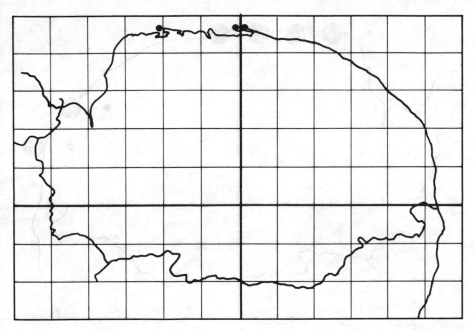

Arctic Tern

Sterna paradisaea

Tetrads recorded in: 3 *(<1%)*
Possible breeding: nil
Probable breeding: nil
Confirmed breeding: 3 (100%)

A fairly common visitor to the coast, and
one which is occasionally seen inland on
passage. A few pairs have bred in the county in most years since a nest was first located
at Blakeney Point in 1922. During the
NBBS, up to six pairs have bred at this
traditional site, together with no more than
one in any single year at Scolt Head. (The
Blakeney Point records originated from two
tetrads there.)

Arctic Terns are superficially similar in
appearance to their far more numerous relation (in Norfolk), the Common Tern.
While most birdwatchers should be able to
tell these birds apart when seen clearly in
good light, away from the reserves where
the breeding terns are carefully monitored
by wardens there is a possibility that the occasional Arctic Tern bred undetected among
a large colony of Common Terns.

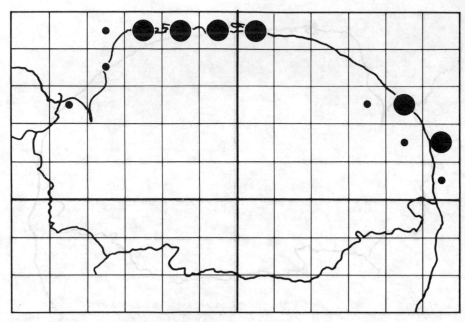

Little Tern

Sterna albifrons

Tetrads recorded in:	43	(3%)
Possible breeding:	18	(42%)
Probable breeding:	3	(7%)
Confirmed breeding:	22	(51%)

Within each 10-km square, the highest category of record(s) received from the tetrads therein has been plotted centrally. All who care for the well-being of this at-risk summer visitor will appreciate the cautious approach adopted in the *Norfolk Bird Atlas.*

This is an established visitor to the sand and shingle beaches of the county, although it does not nest where such beaches are backed by cliffs. Breeding also occurred on Scroby Sands off Great Yarmouth between 1955 and 1963 and again in 1976, a site subsequently lost through tidal inundation. Less usually, it visits the coastal Broads such as Hickling, where it has bred in recent years.

The breeding population of this tern varied between about 330 and 470 pairs during the NBBS. This is well up to the average for recent decades: however, this attractive seabird is less inclined to breed more or less exclusively within reserves than the other terns, and this means that it is constantly at risk from the activities of egg-collectors, as well as from accidental human disturbance. Nests are also lost in most years through their being overwhelmed by wind-blown sand or exceptionally high tides.

This species is protected in Great Britain at all times by special penalties under Schedule 1, Part I of the Wildlife and Countryside Act, 1981.

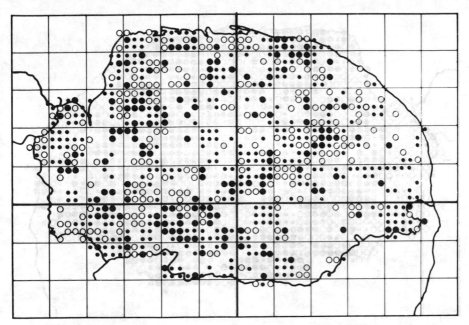

Stock Dove

Columba oenas

Tetrads recorded in:	721	(50%)
Possible breeding:	335	(46%)
Probable breeding:	227	(31%)
Confirmed breeding:	159	(22%)

This species was found by NBBS workers in one-half of the tetrads. There is a suspicion that it was slightly under-recorded, due to some observers failing to pick it out on every occasion from its larger and more abundant — yet somewhat similar — relative the Woodpigeon. As with other members of the *Columbidae*, it has a highly visual display flight — including a butterfly-type aerial dance of paired birds — and records of singing or displaying within suitable habitats are virtually certain to have represented actual nesting. The high percentage of possible breeding records for the Stock Dove in many instances derive from birds briefly dashing past an observer's field of view.

This is a species found in well-wooded country, parkland and scrub, but which avoids thick plantations. A hole nester, it breeds in isolated buildings, trees, dry pits and burrows. Breckland, in particular the 'Battle Area', is much frequented. It is also widespread on chalk scrubland in the north-west of the county and in the well-timbered country between Norwich and Cromer.

55

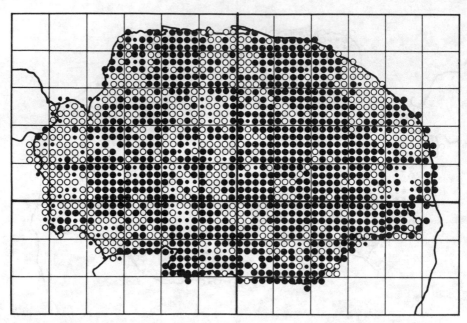

Woodpigeon

Columba palumbus

Tetrads recorded in:	1,401	(96%)
Possible breeding:	98	(7%)
Probable breeding:	446	(32%)
Confirmed breeding:	857	(61%)

The third most widespread bird as established by the NBBS, it was absent from few tetrads other than inhospitable coastal locations and Halvergate Levels. Trees, hedges and bushes provided nesting sites and were exploited almost anywhere from the heavily built-up centres of Norwich and Great Yarmouth to the densest Breckland plantations.

As would have been expected for such a common bird with a wide choice of nest sites, breeding was proved in a high percentage of tetrads. In the vast majority of the remaining squares, calling or displaying birds are sure to have bred too.

In respect of Schedule 2, Part II, of the Wildlife and Countryside Act 1981, this species may be killed by authorised persons at all times — a provision which also extends to the destruction of its nests, eggs and young. This culling is understandably carried out by many Norfolk landowners and occupiers, together with those that they have authorised; it is unlikely, however, that such destruction is so thorough that it has made any mark upon the way that the bird was logged by NBBS workers.

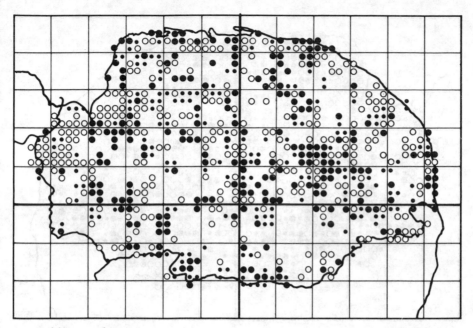

Collared Dove

Streptopelia decaocto

Tetrads recorded in:	683	(47%)
Possible breeding:	175	(26%)
Probable breeding:	283	(41%)
Confirmed breeding:	225	(33%)

A common and sometimes abundant resident in many districts, although it has not (yet) colonised some areas with ostensibly suitable habitats. Indeed, it was found in under one-half of the county's tetrads during six years of fieldwork, and there appears to be some suspicion that its continued expansion, even if it has not completely stalled, is but a slow one. All the same, this species' range did expand rapidly following its initial breeding at Cromer in 1955, and it now inhabits all of Norfolk's towns and many of its villages. It is also found about grain silos, maltings, docks and quays, farm complexes, poultry runs and game pens.

As this species is mostly found in close proximity to human dwellings or other edifices, where it tends to nest in shrub-beries and evergreen and fruit trees, has a distinctive call and a highly visible display flight, NBBS workers could hardly have missed it. Most records of probable breeding which were submitted are likely to have related to nesting, but the actual nests of singing and displaying birds were often hard to pinpoint.

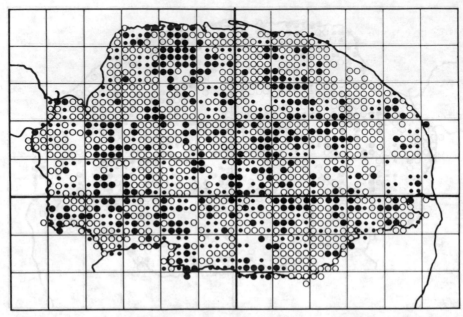

Turtle Dove

Streptopelia turtur

Tetrads recorded in:	1,178	(81%)
Possible breeding:	217	(18%)
Probable breeding:	672	(57%)
Confirmed breeding:	289	(25%)

The most widespread non-passerine summer visitor to Norfolk, this attractive dove returns to its favoured resort of arable but well-timbered farmland in late April and early May. Fumitory seeds provide its staple diet, and this plant is closely associated with the disturbed soils of cultivated land. Nests are built in thick hedgerows, bushes and shrubs, so the population of this species naturally drops when such sites are grubbed up and a prairie landscape ensues. The map shows gaps which mirror this kind of highly intensive arable farming about Fersfield, Guestwick and Trunch.

Most probable breeding records, usually derived from singing or displaying birds, should relate to actual nesting. This was in fact proved in a lower percentage of the tetrads in which this species occurred than in respect of its close relative, the Collared Dove, which was found to have a much less widespread distribution; however, the latter was much more likely to nest in and about human habitations which observers could check with ease. Indeed, the aversion of the Turtle Dove to built-up areas can be seen by the blank spaces in and about Norwich and Great Yarmouth on the map.

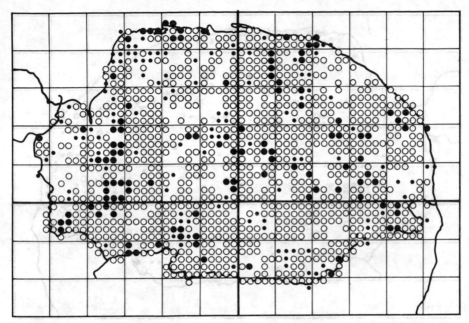

Cuckoo

Cuculus canorus

Tetrads recorded in:	1,095	(75%)
Possible breeding:	112	(10%)
Probable breeding:	871	(80%)
Confirmed breeding:	112	(10%)

The arrival of the Cuckoo from its winter quarters in Africa during April seems to excite more interest amongst the public in general than in respect of any other summer visitor. Once this bird has announced its presence by its familiar call, spring is regarded as having truly arrived — even if this county has still to witness an occasional snow flurry.

It is generally recognised that the Cuckoo has declined in numbers in the last few decades: Seago (*Birds of Norfolk*) having noted this in 1967, for instance. Given its unmistakable call, there can hardly be a tetrad in which this bird was overlooked. Yet, absence which once would have been restricted to built-up areas is now apparent in localities where hedgerows and marginal habitats have been removed in the interests of intensive arable farming.

Juvenile birds only become a familiar sight once they have wandered some way from their nests in late summer. Only 10% of records relate to proved breeding with young having been seen in the nest or immediately after leaving it. In tetrad TG42Q (Hickling Green), young were recorded in the nests of both the commonest host species: Dunnock and Reed Warbler.

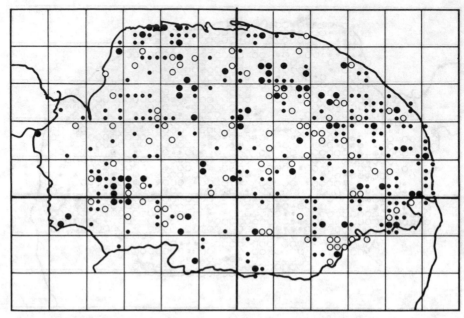

Barn Owl

Tyto alba

Tetrads recorded in:	340	(23%)
Possible breeding:	190	(56%)
Probable breeding:	81	(24%)
Confirmed breeding:	69	(20%)

A widespread resident, most familiar to non-ornithologists at dusk when it is picked up in the headlights of motor vehicles. Indeed, many Barn Owls die through colliding with traffic on roads. This traditional bird of farmland has suffered in recent decades through loss of habitat, including the grubbing-up of old pasture with its wealth of rodent prey. More disastrous were the effects of toxic seed dressings during the late 1950s and early 1960s, menaces which were happily stopped or severely limited through legislation. This species can now be described as holding its own, thanks in part to well-wishers providing nest boxes in modern barns which otherwise are less well adapted to the Barn Owl's needs than the old style structures which were so suitable.

This bird is generally sedentary, and given that many brief sightings could not be followed up a high proportion of the records of probable and even possible breeding ought to have related to successful nesting. Broadland is no longer so marked a stronghold, doubtless due to the demolition of barns, windpumps and other isolated buildings. The upper Bure catchment area seems particularly well favoured and may hold descendants of former Broadland birds. This species was doubtless underrecorded in certain districts which were not surveyed at dusk — much of the upper Wissey Valley, for instance.

The Barn Owl is protected in Great Britain at all times by special penalties under Schedule 1, Part I of the Wildlife and Countryside Act, 1981.

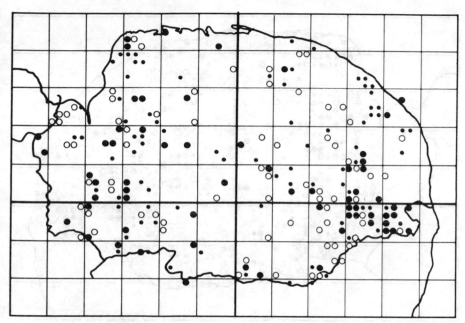

Little Owl

Athene noctua

Tetrads recorded in:	225	(15%)
Possible breeding:	84	(37%)
Probable breeding:	77	(34%)
Confirmed breeding:	64	(28%)

Introduced to Norfolk in the 19th century, this species first became widespread in the 1920s — by the end of which decade it had become a frequent adornment of the gamekeeper's gibbet. Despite such persecution, Little Owls became familiar denizens of the county's traditional — yet in many areas, post-enclosure — agricultural landscape in which most fields were surrounded by thriving hedges dotted with mature deciduous trees. The trend, which accelerated from about 1950, towards larger field units and the consequent eradication of such hedges and trees was paralleled by a decline in this bird's population. Since the later 1970s, a reversal of this decline has been observed in some areas: this welcome fact perhaps due in part to the active manner in which many farmers are now involved with habitat conservation programmes.

The NBBS has revealed that this species is most widespread in and to the south-east of the Chet Valley. This area, which includes some stiff boulder-clay soils, retains much wood-pasture landscape — hedged fields and closes well endowed with oaks and ashes. Elsewhere, the Little Owl was less concentrated for the most part, yet found to be sufficiently widespread to further the hope that with public opinion in favour of conservation measures it may re-occupy its former range.

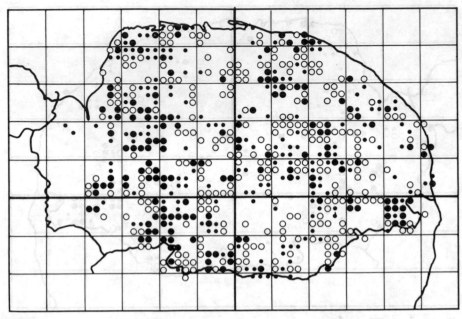

Tawny Owl

Strix aluco

Tetrads recorded in:	584	(40%)
Possible breeding:	168	(29%)
Probable breeding:	262	(45%)
Confirmed breeding:	154	(26%)

This, the most common breeding owl, was found in more tetrads than the Barn Owl and the Little Owl — the second and third most widespread species — put together. Away from the Fens and open areas of Broadland, most parts of the county which are at least reasonably well wooded have resident Tawny Owls — indeed, some occur in towns where parks, cemeteries and the large gardens associated with certain inner suburbs are favoured.

Tawny Owls are not often encountered in daylight — save when accidentally disturbed — but their presence is easily established by the familiar hooting. Newly fledged owlets are noisy, and their *kewick* calls were recognised by many observers. Breeding was confirmed in more tetrads in the west of the county than in the east, thanks to such records having been made during a specific survey of Long-eared Owl sites which was carried out independently of the NBBS — data by courtesy of J.B. Kemp

Being highly territorial and sedentary, most records of this species which fell short of confirming breeding would doubtless have related to it.

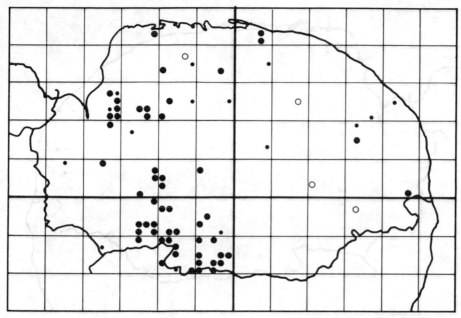

Long-eared Owl

Asio otus

Tetrads recorded in:	75	*(5%)*
Possible breeding:	16	(21%)
Probable breeding:	4	(5%)
Confirmed breeding:	55	(73%)

A record of confirmed breeding in the TF61 10-km square, other than the one shown above, has not been mapped at the request of the observer concerned.

A scarce resident which also occurs in small numbers as a passage migrant and winter visitor. It is prone to predation by the larger Tawny Owl, a bird of deciduous woodland, and avoids this for the most part by frequenting coniferous trees in both plantations and shelter belts. A decline in the population of the Long-eared Owl was probably stemmed during the inter-war years with their major afforestation programme, mostly although not solely concerning Breckland.

This is the most nocturnal of a largely nocturnal family, and it may well have been missed — especially in the east of the county — by observers who did not make special efforts to seek it out. During 1980 and 1981, and to a lesser extent in the two years following, special surveys were carried out in West Norfolk (which contains the most suitable habitats) under the leadership of J.B. Kemp — who kindly supplied the NBBS with data. Breeding, which was established through hearing the hunger calls of the young, was confirmed at thirty-four sites in 1980 and in only one fewer during 1981.

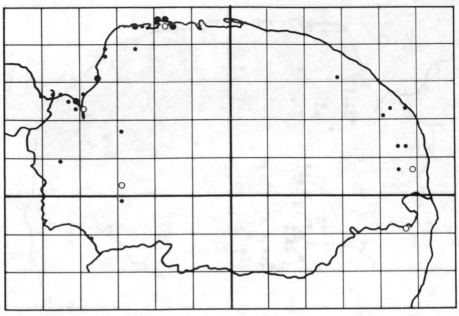

Short-eared Owl

Asio flammeus

Tetrads recorded in:	33	(2%)
Possible breeding:	22	(67%)
Probable breeding:	5	(15%)
Confirmed breeding:	6	(18%)

A very few Short-eared Owls breed in the county most years, although this bird is more common as a passage migrant and winter visitor (and even abundant whenever there is an abundance of its favoured prey, the Short-tailed Vole). This is a denizen of wild, open country, and breeding records have usually been restricted to the north coast, the Wash, Fenland, Breckland and Broadland. During the NBBS, only the first two of these areas produced confirmed records, although the last two had one and two probable instances respectively. Due to the somewhat inaccessible sites of two of these last records, there are grounds for hoping that this handsome owl did breed in at least one of them.

Two-thirds of the records submitted by observers concerned possible breeding. It is unlikely that any of these did in fact relate to actual nesting, for most emanated from areas which were watched regularly — the Broads and the sea-banks of the Wash. The birds seen in these instances were almost certainly unmated wanderers.

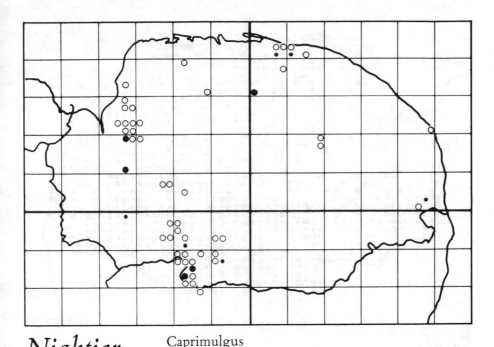

Nightjar

Caprimulgus europaeus

Tetrads recorded in:	58	*(4%)*
Possible breeding:	6	(10%)
Probable breeding:	47	(81%)
Confirmed breeding:	5	(9%)

This summer visitor, which tends not to arrive until early May, frequents heathland with scattered trees, clearfell areas in forestry and young coniferous plantations, especially where there is a good ground layer of bracken. Sand-dunes which have become well-fixed with vegetation are sometimes frequented, although only one such instance was forthcoming during the NBBS — from tetrad TG42Z (Winterton Dunes). The Nightjar was once common in districts having its favoured habitats, but a decrease in its numbers was noted by Seago in 1967 (*Birds of Norfolk*). Data plotted on the relevant map in the BTO/IWC *Atlas* might imply that numbers were still high during that survey period on 1968-1972; however, this was based upon the 10-km square, each of which contains twenty-five tetrads. The above map, based on the latter unit, does reflect a real contraction in the Nightjar's range — especially in the eastern half of the county. This contraction is in line with a national trend, and would seem to have little to do with habitat loss for this has in fact been stemmed or even halted in recent years.

This species remains well-established in Breckland — including the Suffolk Brecks, its British stronghold — and the well-wooded heathland and warrens on the Lower Cretaceous in the hinterland of King's Lynn, but it is now noticably less common about the Cromer-Holt ridge and has entirely deserted such a traditional site as Marsham Heath. It is not easy to prove breeding for this crepuscular and nocturnal bird, but most of the probable breeding records relate to churring individuals which for the most part may be equated to nesting pairs. A BTO survey in 1981 revealed 145 churring birds in West Norfolk and 16 or 17 in the east of the county.

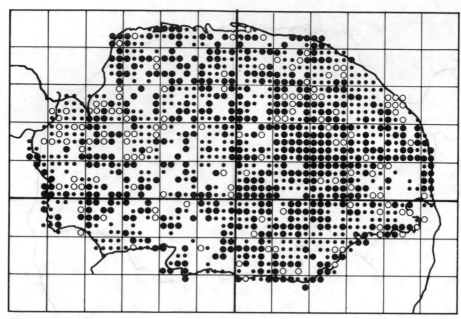

Swift

Apus apus

Tetrads recorded in:	1,098	(75%)
Possible breeding:	450	(41%)
Probable breeding:	133	(12%)
Confirmed breeding:	515	(47%)

The presence of the Swift as it sweeps through the sky from May to August is such a familiar sight that it is almost taken for granted. This bird spends its entire life in the air (barring accidents), save when attending its nest, so observers should not have entered it upon NBBS record cards unless it was seen in the vicinity of buildings offering suitable nesting sites. The nests of this bird are not often found while they are occupied — indeed, it is illegal to seek them actively — but proof of breeding was readily determined through the adults' regular visits to apparent sites.

Confirmed breeding records on the map in general indicate tetrads containing towns and villages, although some nesting sites may be in isolated buildings such as chur-

ches. A few Swifts exploit traditional cliff sites at Hunstanton in most years. Even where breeding was not confirmed, it almost certainly occurred given suitable buildings: for instance, it is hardly conceivable that nesting did not take place successfully in all the populous villages of the Marshland (silt Fens) west and south-west of King's Lynn.

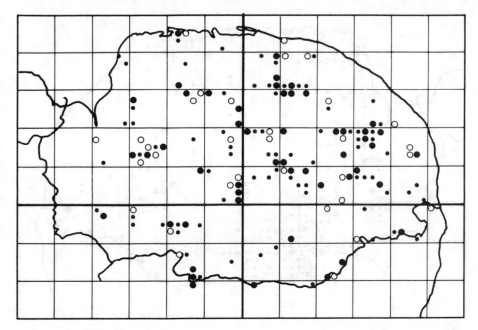

Kingfisher

Alcedo atthis

Tetrads recorded in:	158	(11%)
Possible breeding:	75	(47%)
Probable breeding:	33	(21%)
Confirmed breeding:	50	(32%)

A widespread resident along many of Norfolk's waterways, including lakes and gravel pits. No records were forthcoming from the Fens west of the Great Ouse and south of the Wissey, whence some were submitted during the BTO/IWC *Atlas* project of 1968-1972. In severe winters, which affected the NBBS period of 1980-1985 rather more than the BTO/IWC project, this bird suffers badly from the icing-up of inland waters. Fortunately, as it has a high reproductive potential and many birds remove to tidal creeks where icing is less prevalent during the winter months, it shows an ability to maintain a steady population level overall.

During the breeding season, this species is sedentary and many of the records shown on the above map which fell short of confirmed breeding ought to relate to this. Nest sites were often easy to find in suitable tetrads which were thoroughly worked throughout the NBBS. Where tetrads were surveyed less exhaustively, brief sightings of this species could not always be followed up.

This bird is protected in Great Britain at all times by special penalties under Schedule 1, Part I of the Wildlife and Countryside Act, 1981.

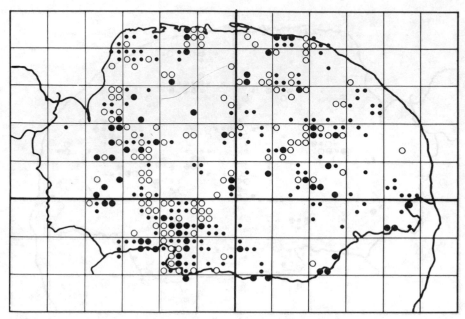

Green Woodpecker

Picus viridis

Tetrads recorded in:	331	(23%)
Possible breeding:	149	(45%)
Probable breeding:	116	(35%)
Confirmed breeding:	66	(20%)

While it is still a fairly common resident in some districts, this handsome bird's range has contracted in recent years — indeed, it has all but vanished from the south and west-centre of the county since the BTO/IWC *Atlas* project of 1968-1972. This species favours well-wooded countryside, including parkland and dry heathland with scattered trees, with a substantial component of well-cropped grassland. The loss of such habitats due to land reclamation, together with the relatively low rabbit population which has obtained since myxomatosis first struck in the mid-1950s have contributed to the Green Woodpecker's decline.

Breckland has always provided the best country for this species and it is even more marked as its stronghold today. Other favoured areas which still have good numbers include the tract of woods with heathland which extends north-north-west from Breckland towards Hunstanton, and heavily timbered pockets of countryside from Sheringham south to the environs of Norwich. Being sedentary during the breeding season, successful nesting doubtless occurred in many tetrads from which possible and probable records were submitted.

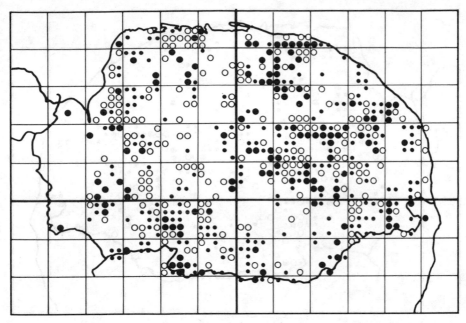

Great Spotted Woodpecker   Dendrocopos major

Tetrads recorded in:	538	(37%)
Possible breeding:	202	(38%)
Probable breeding:	204	(38%)
Confirmed breeding:	132	(25%)

The most common and widely distributed woodpecker, this bird has by all accounts increased in numbers over the last twenty years — perhaps largely as a consequence of the sad complement of dead elms which offer a home for its invertebrate food and which the countryside now contains in some quantity. The author's own sightings of this species in the parishes of Drayton, Costessey, Taverham, Felthorpe, Horsford and Hellesdon between 1964 and 1972 were only 50% of those of the Green Woodpecker, but his subsequent sightings ratio has been exactly reversed. No complete 10-km square outside Fenland failed to produce a Great Spotted Woodpecker record, a bird once mostly confined to woodland proper but which NBBS workers frequently noted along well-timbered hedgerows and in gardens in town and country alike.

Seeing adults with food for their young was the source of most confirmed breeding records, although with practice it was not too difficult to identify the holes of all the woodpecker species from their relative sizes. A high proportion of non-confirmed records should relate to actual breeding in respect of this widespread and generally sedentary bird.

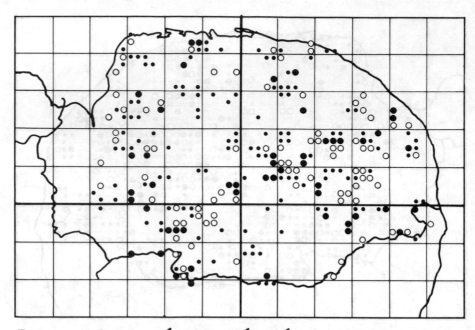

Lesser Spotted Woodpecker Dendrocopos minor

Tetrads recorded in:	265	(18%)
Possible breeding:	131	(49%)
Probable breeding:	84	(32%)
Confirmed breeding:	50	(19%)

Seago, writing in 1967 (*Birds of Norfolk*), described this bird as 'a scarce breeding resident'; however, the NBBS has established that it is a not uncommon resident in many parts of the county. The scarcity once attributed to this species would seem to have derived in part from its small size taken together with its liking for the small branches within the canopy of mature deciduous trees. That there has been a definite increase in its numbers over the last twenty years has been remarked upon by most observers, an increase particularly linked to the greater availability of invertebrate food provided by the still growing numbers of Dutch elm disease victims.

The nest holes of this bird were not easily traced, according to many NBBS workers,

and rather more records of confirmed breeding were derived from seeing newly fledged young. This is a particularly sedentary species, and it is therefore likely that a high proportion of the records submitted which fell short of confirmed breeding in fact related to this. Indeed, it is also likely that some observers totally overlooked this charming, Chaffinch-sized woodpecker in some tetrads which had suitable habitat.

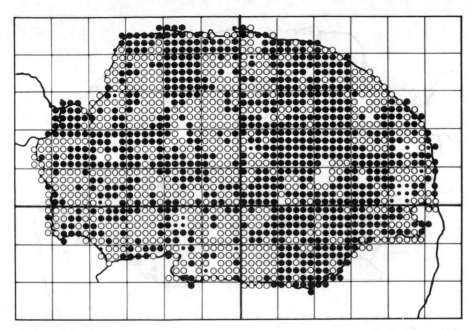

Skylark

Alauda arvensis

Tetrads recorded in:	1,408	(97%)
Possible breeding:	22	(2%)
Probable breeding:	613	(44%)
Confirmed breeding:	773	(55%)

The second most widespread species as established by the NBBS, its loud and unmistakable song tending to pinpoint its presence initially. Norfolk is for the larger part a county of relatively open landscapes, and hence allows for a vast area of suitable nesting habitat for this bird. Apart from arable land and rough pasture, Skylarks also breed on waste ground and can penetrate those parts of urban areas which contain this — their absence from inner Norwich is, however, apparent. Of the scatter of tetrads in which this species was not noted, a few relate to dense plantations, but patches of newly planted conifers may hold breeding Skylarks for the first year or two.

Given the existence of suitable habitat, this bird is so common that most records which fell short of confirming breeding are still likely to relate to it. Breeding was in any case easy to establish, for adults carry food to their young in a way which is readily visible and will give distraction displays when their fledglings are threatened.

RM.

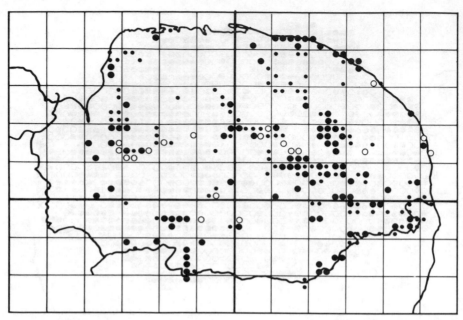

Sand Martin

Riparia riparia

Tetrads recorded in:	223	(15%)
Possible breeding:	103	(46%)
Probable breeding:	20	(9%)
Confirmed breeding:	100	(45%)

This is one of our earliest summer visitors, being observed for the first time well before the end of March in most years — although breeding sites tend not to be prospected until mid-April. This species' population 'crashed' between 1968 and 1969, its numbers having been depleted mainly by the drought which afflicted (and which continues to afflict) its wintering quarters in the Sahel zone of Africa. Indeed, a further drop in numbers which doubtless could be related to the same persistent disaster was noted between the 1983 and 1984 seasons. This latter drop certainly influenced adversely the amount of records of this bird gathered from tetrads not surveyed until the final two NBBS years — in particular, large tracts of the Fens. Certainly, this species is now less widely distributed in Norfolk than it was during the BTO/IWC Atlas survey of 1968-1972.

This hole-nesting bird — it may excavate its own or utilise existing ones — often breeds in large colonies. Its favourite locations are banks in both worked-out and active gravel pits, together with boulder-clay cliffs, and the banks of rivers and streams — especially upstream of Broadland. Suitable man-made structures such as drainage pipes are also used, for example by the Wensum in central Norwich.

Swallow

Hirundo rustica

Tetrads recorded in:	1,386	(95%)
Possible breeding:	109	(8%)
Probable breeding:	68	(5%)
Confirmed breeding:	1,209	(87%)

This eagerly awaited harbinger of spring is first noted in early April in most years, although it is not until the third week of that month before the bird appears in good numbers and begins to prospect old nesting sites — which it has a tendency to remain faithful to in successive seasons. This was found to be the most widespread summer visitor (and the sixth most widespread breeding bird), one able to exploit a wide range of man-made sites in respect of building its mud-cup nests. It is highly tolerant of man's presence and often noisy activities. Farm buildings, sheds, country stations and occasionally occupied houses are all favoured for nesting sites.

Both occupied and used nests are easy to spot, and the map not only shows a widespread range but also the high proportion of confirmed breeding records — indeed, the fourth highest total of all the county's birds. Many tetrads in which breeding confirmation was not established were either surveyed in haste or had few likely nesting sites; those with no records tended to lack any such locations. Two tetrads in inner Norwich, TG20B and F, only had presence noted which is likely to be an accurate expression of the Swallow's status there.

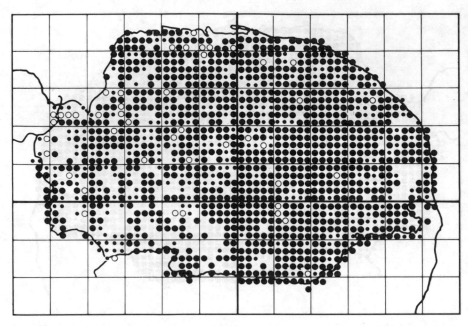

House Martin

Delichon urbica

Tetrads recorded in:	1,234	(85%)
Possible breeding:	215	(17%)
Probable breeding:	45	(4%)
Confirmed breeding:	974	(79%)

As familiar a summer visitor as the Swallow, the House Martin is nevertheless not so widespread in respect of its breeding range. Arriving about a week later than its close relative, this bird has a longer incubation and fledging period and young from later broods may still be seen being fed in mid-October.

Given the facts that its mud nests are distinctive and, unlike those of the Swallow, affixed to readily viewed external masonry of houses and other suitable edifices, breeding was likewise easy to prove. That a smaller percentage of confirmed records were established by NBBS workers would thus seem to be a further indication of the smaller numbers in which this species occurs. Unlike the Swallow, the House Martin was found to nest in small numbers in the inner Norwich tetrads.

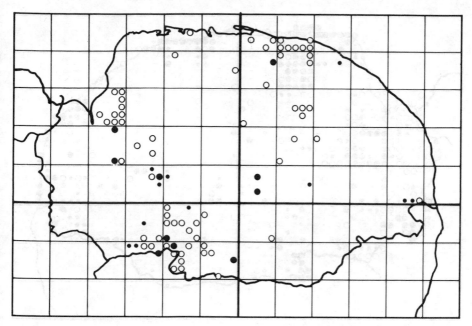

Tree Pipit

Anthus trivialis

Tetrads recorded in:	87	(6%)
Possible breeding:	11	(13%)
Probable breeding:	66	(76%)
Confirmed breeding:	10	(11%)

A somewhat scarce summer visitor, unknown in many districts although favoured areas often possess small concentrations. This species requires a combination of tall trees from which it can start its parachuting song-flight with grass and bracken nearby for feeding and nesting purposes. Open deciduous woodland, young coniferous plantations in which a few mature deciduous trees are left standing, and well-wooded heathland are particularly favoured. In Norfolk, Breckland was found to have the largest concentration of Tree Pipits, while smaller numbers were found in contiguous tetrads about the lower cretaceous to the east of King's Lynn and the morainic soils in the hinterland of Sheringham.

As long as suitable habitat is retained, this species is particularly loyal to a site. For instance, isolated tetrads in which probable breeding was noted at Felthorpe and Horsford (TG11H and TG21F) have held up to four pairs each since at least as far back as the early 1960s. Unless the adults are seen with their young, it is hard to prove breeding for this bird. Most probable breeding records should relate to actual nesting.

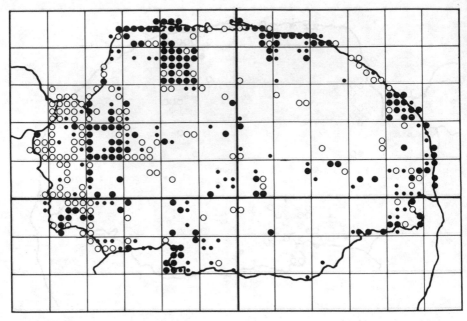

Meadow Pipit

Anthus pratensis

Tetrads recorded in:	400	(27%)
Possible breeding:	103	(26%)
Probable breeding:	140	(35%)
Confirmed breeding:	157	(35%)

Unlike the Tree Pipit, this is a resident species — albeit one with numbers reinforced by passage birds and winter visitors. Indeed, and especially in severe weather, some inland areas are forsaken for Broadland, the Fens and coastal districts. This bird has a somewhat scattered breeding distribution, and whilst it is common in a wide range of habitats it is scarce or absent in extensive tracts of country. Its tinkling song, given in a parachuting display flight, was readily noted by observers in many tetrads with rough grassland, marshes with drier patches, cliff-top pasture, sand-dunes and young forestry plantations — or even in mature plantations with broad, grassy rides.

The scatter of records away from its main range, often from farmland, were sometimes noted almost by accident, for the Meadow Pipit can be inconspicuous when it is not singing/displaying. Heavy clays and the stiffer loams are mostly avoided, a fact noted in the tetrad surveys of Bedfordshire and Kent as well as here in Norfolk. The grubbing up of rough pasture has slightly reduced its range, although it is quite tolerant of human activity. Breeding was proved, for example, on the well-trodden dunes of Blakeney and waste ground in some Norwich suburbs.

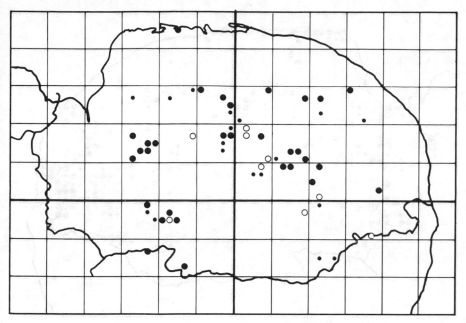

Grey Wagtail

Motacilla cinerea

Tetrads recorded in:	*58*	*(4%)*
Possible breeding:	18	(31%)
Probable breeding:	9	(16%)
Confirmed breeding:	31	(53%)

An uncommon summer visitor, passage migrant and winter visitor. This was first known to breed in the county at Taverham Mill in 1921, a locality still frequented. Water-mills and weirs along rivers and streams are favoured nesting locations, although old-fashioned bridges with loose and crumbling brickwork also produced records. An instance of breeding at Cantley Beet Factory was the only atypical one to come out of the NBBS.

Numbers of breeding pairs tend to fluctuate from year to year particularly following severe winters. It is pleasing to be able to state that the trend is towards an increase and this handsome bird is now more numerous than it has ever been. NBBS workers found it in twenty-five 10-km squares, compared with only eleven during the BTO/IWC *Atlas* project of 1968-1972.

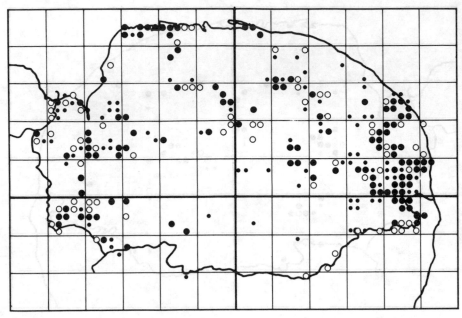

Yellow Wagtail

Motacilla flava

Tetrads recorded in:	272	(19%)
Possible breeding:	85	(31%)
Probable breeding:	70	(26%)
Confirmed breeding:	117	(43%)

One of our most attractive summer visitors, the Yellow Wagtail sometimes arrives in late March but it can be more confidently expected in early April. This is a bird which has adapted to a wide range of habitats, although it is most widespread on Broadland, Fenland and coastal levels and grazing marshes. It also favours meadows by rivers and streams outside those areas. NBBS workers also found this species at sewage works and on two Breckland heaths, on fruit farms and inland root-fields.

This bird was declining in numbers in 1967, when Seago wrote *Birds of Norfolk*, and this would still appear to be the case. Of the complete 10-km squares in the county — that is those having a full complement

of twenty-five tetrads covered by the NBBS — nine failed to produce a single Yellow Wagtail record during the 1980-1985 period, compared with four during the BTO/IWC *Atlas* project of 1968-1972. The trend towards monocultural grassland in place of semi-natural inland pasture has militated against this bird, one which remains relatively common on the traditional wetland pasture of Broadland, for example.

A male of the Blue-headed race, *flava*, successfully raised fledglings at Holme in 1983, although oddly enough no female was seen.

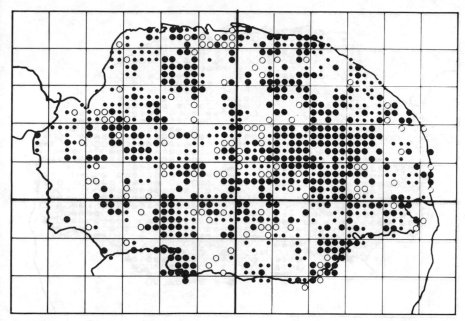

Pied Wagtail

Motacilla alba

Tetrads recorded in:	770	(53%)
Possible breeding:	271	(35%)
Probable breeding:	105	(14%)
Confirmed breeding:	394	(51%)

A common and widespread resident and passage migrant, although somewhat decreased in recent years due to changes in agricultural practices — an example of such being the trend towards the sanatization of the once fly-ridden traditional farmyard! This bird was once all but ubiquitous in non-woodland habitat; the NBBS has indicated that it has now deserted some not inconsiderable tracts of country, especially those where the farmland has taken on a 'prairie' aspect — and in this respect one has to include much of the Fens and parts of the once lush levels of Broadland.

Most records of confirmed breeding were derived from seeing adults with insect food for their young — often picked up from road surfaces. The Pied Wagtail does not have a well developed song, and this probably accounts for the far higher number of possible as opposed to probable breeding records which were submitted. In both such cases, breeding would actually have occurred in many instances for this is a particularly sedentary bird during the nesting season.

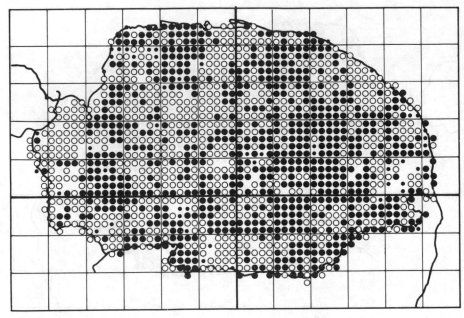

Wren

Troglodytes troglodytes

Tetrads recorded in:	1,358	*(93%)*
Possible breeding:	50	(4%)
Probable breeding:	622	(46%)
Confirmed breeding:	686	(51%)

A common and sometimes abundant, near ubiquitous resident. This is a bird which NBBS observers would have expected to find in all tetrads, excepting only those with insufficient cover to afford nesting sites. Areas shown on the map where this latter factor obtained are Halvergate Levels, coastal saltmarshes, and a few localities within the Fens. This species is very likely to have been overlooked in tetrads elsewhere which show absence.

During the BTO/IWC *Atlas* survey of 1968-1972, the Wren was not only found to be the third most widespread bird but was also considered to have been the most numerous. That project was undertaken following and during a sequence of years with no severe winters. Sadly, the Wren is seriously affected by long cold spells and these did have a bearing upon the NBBS. First, this species would not have completely recovered from the severe conditions of the early part of 1979 by the time of the first NBBS season, 1980; while in addition the bitter conditions which obtained during December 1981, February 1983, and January and February 1985 would have depressed the numbers available for breeding in the subsequent seasons. This species does have the ability to recover its numbers, given a run of two or more winters with no worse than average conditions prevailing.

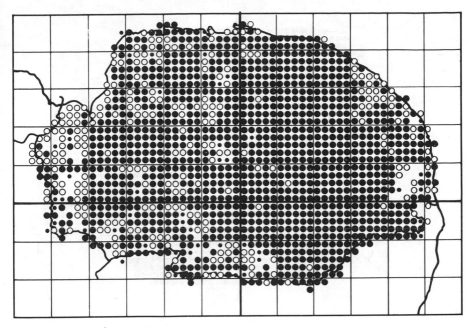

Dunnock

Prunella modularis

Tetrads recorded in:	1,383	(95%)
Possible breeding:	48	(3%)
Probable breeding:	244	(18%)
Confirmed breeding:	1,091	(79%)

A familiar and near-ubiquitous resident, recorded in the seventh highest number of tetrads. Essentially an undistinguished-looking bird, although attractively marked when viewed from close range, observers would have noted its squeeky song and distinctive wing-flicking habits announcing the establishment of territory from late winter.

This species is only genuinely absent from tetrads lacking cover for it to nest in: these including coastal locations, especially salt-marshes, and open areas of the Fens and Broadland — most obviously Halvergate Levels. A scatter of blank tetrads in and about Breckland probably held a few Dunnocks which were missed by observers; nearly all non-proven records should concern successful nesting, as this is a particularly sedentary species.

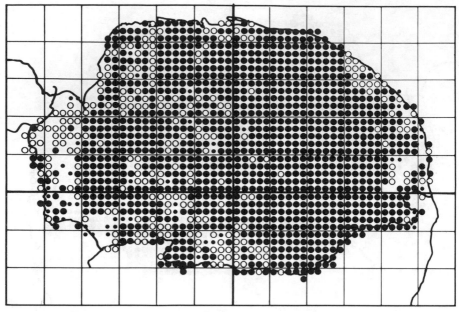

Robin

Erithacus rubecula

Tetrads recorded in:	1,350	(93%)
Possible breeding:	47	(3%)
Probable breeding:	234	(17%)
Confirmed breeding:	1,069	(79%)

The much-loved Robin, Britain's national bird, could hardly have been missed by any NBBS worker. It may therefore come as a surprise to those who take its presence — even its company — for granted that it just missed out having been located in the ten highest number of tetrads. Its range is similar to that of the Dunnock, but it is likely to exploit isolated favourable sites in open land and certain coastal districts — for instance, many a cliff-top bramble patch was found to hold Dunnocks but not Robins. One observer noted that for no apparent reason, most ostensibly favourable gardens in the stretch of land between the former A17 road and the south shore of The Wash lacked Robins.

Most possible and probable breeding records are likely to have related to successful nesting, for this bird is generally sedentary in spring.

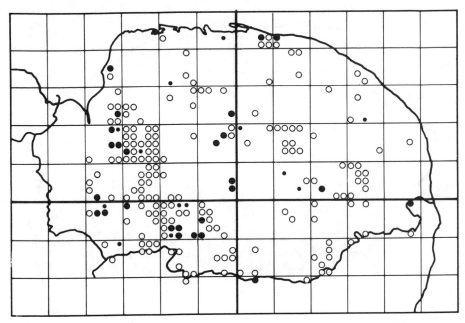

Nightingale

Luscinia megarhyncha

Tetrads recorded in:	212	*(15%)*
Possible breeding:	13	(6%)
Probable breeding:	172	(81%)
Confirmed breeding:	27	(13%)

One record of probable breeding in the TF02 10-km square has not been mapped at the request of the observer concerned.

If it were not for the magnificent song of the male, the arrival of this summer visitor might otherwise be overlooked by most people as it is one of the most skulking of all the county's breeding birds. It frequents dense vegetation in open woodland, overgrown gravel pits, blackthorn thickets and young coniferous plantations. In localities with plenty of suitable cover it can be quite common; for instance, twenty-five singing males were logged within the 120ha (300 acres) of Foulden Common (tetrads TF70 X and Y and TL79 C and D) in a night in late May, 1980. In all, 345 songsters were located at that time throughout the county during a survey organised by the BTO.

Due to its skulking habits, it is particularly difficult to confirm breeding for this species — even within its main range which extends from Breckland north-north-west towards Snettisham. Given that it has a strong tendency to return to suitable sites year after year, one might reasonably suppose that many if not most of the probable breeding records shown above would have related to nesting pairs.

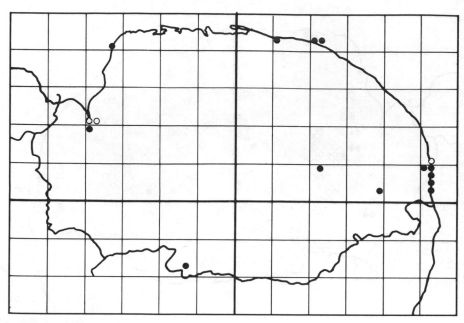

Black Redstart

Phoenicurus ochruros

Tetrads recorded in:	17	*(1%)*	Countryside Act, 1981.
Possible breeding:	nil		
Probable breeding:	4	(24%)	
Confirmed breeding:	13	(76%)	

One record of probable breeding in the TF72 10-km square has not been mapped, following consultations with the observer concerned.

A scarce and local summer visitor, better known as a passage migrant while very few also occur in winter. This bird is first known to have bred in 1950 (Great Yarmouth); breeding has since spread to other urban areas and is now regular or almost regular in some of them. Beet factories have also been chosen for nesting sites on at least two occasions, including one during the NBBS, as have certain military or former military installations.

This species is protected in Great Britain at all times by special penalties under Schedule 1, Part I of the Wildlife and

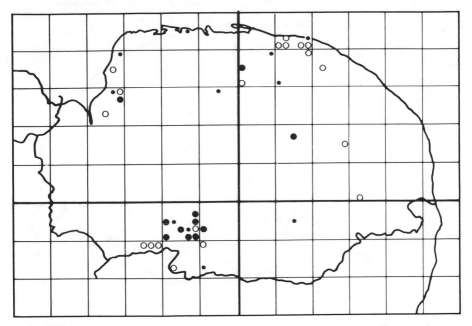

Redstart

Phoenicurus phoenicurus

Tetrads recorded in:	41	(3%)
Possible breeding:	11	(27%)
Probable breeding:	19	(46%)
Confirmed breeding:	11	(27%)

One record of probable breeding in the TL88 10-km square has not been mapped at the request of the observer concerned.

A local and sadly decreasing summer visitor, although still a regular passage migrant. This bird of open mature woodland, both deciduous and mixed, had suffered decreases during the first two-thirds of the present century due to the felling of such habitats — partly motivated by the break-up of a number of great estates. In 1969, a further slump in the numbers returning to Norfolk (and to Britain as a whole) was occasioned by the severe (and continuing) drought in this species' wintering quarters, the Sahel zone of Africa. It has subsequently retreated from the tract of suitable country it had frequented between

Breckland and the woods to the north-east of King's Lynn; and, while it is still reasonably well represented in the Battle Area of northern Breckland, only a few remain in the Sandringham district. The Cromer-Holt ridge, another well-wooded area once favoured, also contained but a few birds by 1985.

Breeding was only confirmed in three tetrads outside Breckland between 1980 and 1985.

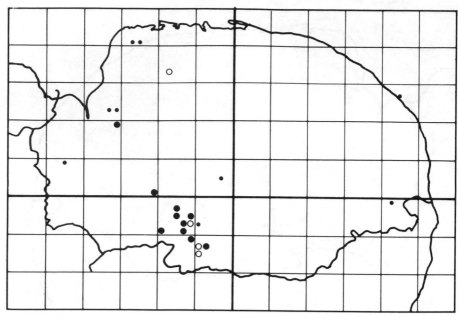

Whinchat

Saxicola rubetra

Tetrads recorded in:	26	(2%)
Possible breeding:	12	(46%)
Probable breeding:	4	(15%)
Confirmed breeding:	10	(38%)

A summer visitor which is very scarce as a breeding bird, although rather more are seen as autumn passage migrants. It favours heathland, rough grazing and gorse clumps, and has lost many of these habitats through land reclamation in the present century. As recently as the BTO/IWC *Atlas* survey of 1968-1972, it occurred widely although in low numbers in the Ouse Washes and other suitable locations in the peat Fens, in Breckland, and in the heathy country extending north-north-westwards from there towards Heacham, as well as in a few coastal sites.

The NBBS has shown that regular breeding is now restricted to Breckland heaths, especially those in the 'Battle Area'. Beyond the Brecks, breeding was established on a single occasion at Leziate in a heathland area formerly much favoured by this bird. A scatter of records from other parts of the county are likely to relate to passage or un-mated birds.

Judging from NBBS cards submitted by observers who worked areas favoured by this species, no more than ten pairs are likely to have bred in the county in any of the years the Survey was running.

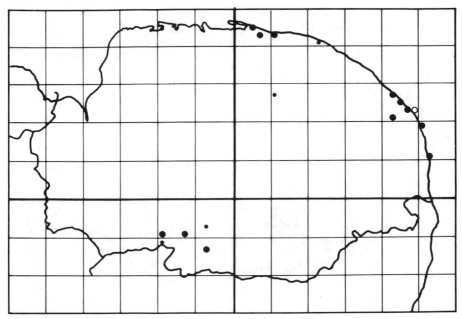

Stonechat

Saxicola torquata

Tetrads recorded in:	19	(1%)
Possible breeding:	6	(32%)
Probable breeding:	1	(5%)
Confirmed breeding:	12	(63%)

Unlike its close relative the Whinchat, the Stonechat is a resident bird. It favours not dissimilar country, although it shows a bias towards rough grazing close to the coast with plenty of gorse clumps and bramble patches. While it is still scarce — indeed, it was found in fewer tetrads than the Whinchat — the Stonechat breeds in somewhat larger numbers: up to twenty pairs annually, judging by the NBBS returns. This means that it has become more common that at any time since the 1930s, when land reclamation first started to reduce its preferred habitats.

This bird now favours two distinct coastal stretches: rough ground at the edge of the marshes between Cley and Weybourne, and the extensive dune com-plex running from Sea Palling to the North Denes at Great Yarmouth — breeding was also registered on one occasion at nearby Hickling. It also bred in three Breckland tetrads between 1980 and 1985, although not annually. Interestingly, these tetrads also held breeding Whinchats.

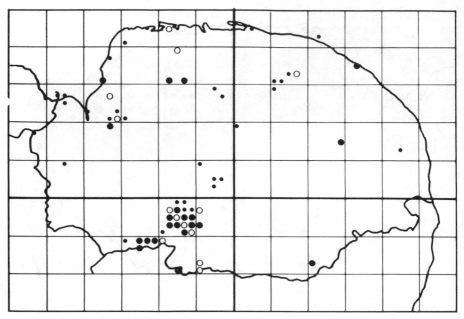

Wheatear

Oenanthe oenanthe

Tetrads recorded in:	65	(4%)
Possible breeding:	32	(49%)
Probable breeding:	12	(18%)
Confirmed breeding:	21	(32%)

A scarce and local summer visitor, far more common and widespread as a passage migrant. This species frequents grassland and heathland, especially wherever grazing by sheep and/or rabbits maintains a short sward. The loss of marginal land during the present century added to the ongoing effect of endemic myxomatosis upon the rabbit population has produced a marked contraction in the Wheatear's breeding range. However, thanks to conservation measures including the somewhat incidental protection afforded by the 'Battle Area' of northern Breckland, it seems that this contraction has been arrested. Certainly, the NBBS data was derived from no fewer localities than that gathered during the BTO/IWC *Atlas* project of 1968-1972.

Away from its Breckland stronghold, the Wheatear has no other regular breeding station in the county. Scattered instances of confirmed breeding are likely to relate to delayed passage birds which exploited localities offering suitable habitat — for instance, rough pasture at a disused airfield in Salhouse parish. Passage birds which did not remain to breed are likely to have provided the majority of the remaining records shown on the map.

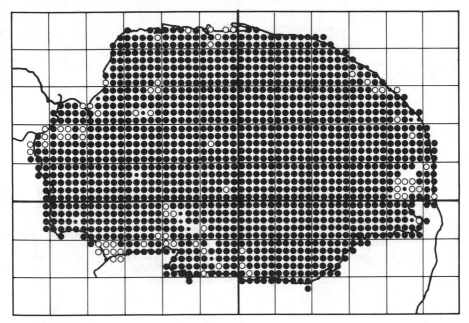

Blackbird

Turdus merula

Tetrads recorded in:	1,422	(98%)
Possible breeding:	18	(1%)
Probable breeding:	71	(5%)
Confirmed breeding:	1,333	(94%)

Not only was the Blackbird the most widespread breeding bird, it was proved to breed in more tetrads than any other. There seems little doubt that this is Norfolk's most common breeding species; the Wren, which was considered to be the most abundant in the 1968-1972 survey period of the BTO/IWC *Atlas*, may well have had the same ranking in respect of our county then but would appear to have suffered a not insignificant drop in numbers due to some severe winters both preceding and during the NBBS.

Only five inland tetrads failed to produce a relevant Blackbird record. Three were in the Halvergate Levels area, in other parts of which breeding was not always proved for this species, and may well relate to genuine absence from this particularly open landscape; two tetrads in the Brecks had at least some suitable habitat, so Blackbirds may just have been overlooked there.

This species occasionally nests out of season: one well-publicised pair built in a Christmas tree at Thorpe station in Norwich at the end of 1984 but failed to produce any young.

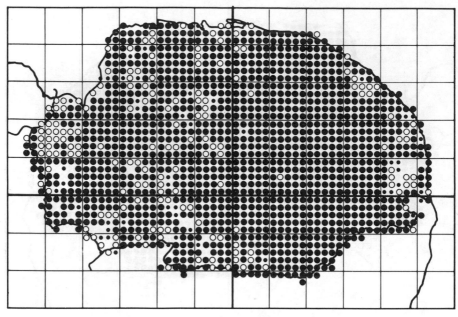

Song Thrush

Turdus philomelos

Tetrads recorded in:	1,394	(96%)
Possible breeding:	53	(4%)
Probable breeding:	164	(12%)
Confirmed breeding:	1,177	(84%)

The fourth most widespread species, as established by the NBBS. This bird, distinctive in appearance, song and behaviour, is one which every child learns to identify, even if they fail to enjoy an interest in ornithology in later life. It is therefore likely that tetrads without any records relate to genuine absence: that is in respect of saltings, open fen, and parts of Halvergate Levels, plus dense coniferous plantations and open heathland in the Brecks.

Areas with suitable habitats — woodland margins, hedgerows, gardens and even isolated bushes as in old marl-pits — where breeding was not proved, were in many instances not visited until the final stages of the Survey, and should otherwise have produced confirmed records. The unmistakable,

mud-lined nest was sometimes discovered out of season and thus proved successful nesting.

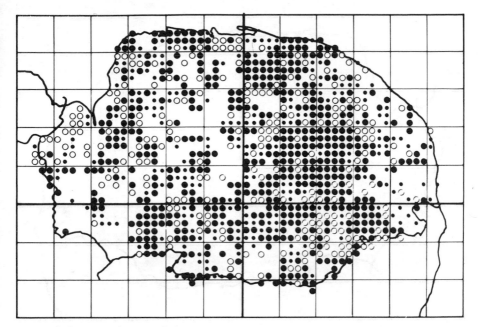

Mistle Thrush

Turdus viscivorus

Tetrads recorded in:	950	(65%)
Possible breeding:	203	(21%)
Probable breeding:	230	(24%)
Confirmed breeding:	517	(54%)

A less familiar sight in small gardens than its close relations, the Blackbird and the Song Thrush, the bold stance of the Mistle Thrush as it sings to announce its territory from midwinter onwards should have attracted the attention of all observers. This is one of the earliest of all Norfolk's birds to nest and young were sometimes spotted in attendance upon their parents two-thirds of the way through March.

Quite common throughout much of its preferred range, wherever there are trees in large gardens, parks and parkland country, and well-wooded areas in general, this bird is scarce or absent from certain districts. The map does indicate a perhaps surprising hint of under-recording. The more open farmland, especially extensive arable, tends to be avoided, as do Broadland levels and marshes and the southern, peat Fens. The Mistle Thrush does find a haven in Broadland villages and the generally more populous silt Fens — the Marshland. A further habitat avoided is the extensive coniferous plantation, although yews and hollies are resorted to.

This species penetrates to the heart of the Norwich urban area; it thus seems strange that it is all but absent from Great Yarmouth.

91

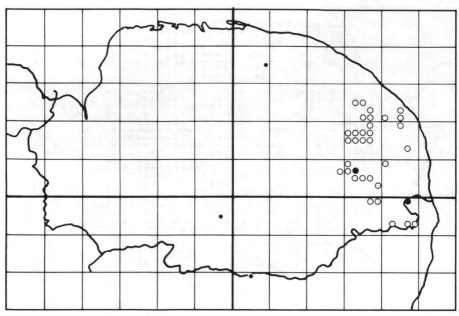

Cetti's Warbler

Cettia cetti

Tetrads recorded in:	37	(3%)
Possible breeding:	3	(8%)
Probable breeding:	32	(86%)
Confirmed breeding:	2	(5%)

This resident warbler was not recorded in Norfolk until 1973, while breeding was first proved in the Yare Valley in the following year. It has since become locally common in Broadland, where it has a liking for tangled vegetation, reed-beds, scrub and carr. It is easily pinpointed through its distinctive song, so the above map is likely to provide a close picture of its range by 1985. Most of the records of probable breeding are sure to relate to nesting pairs; however, not only were NBBS workers laudably loath to risk disturbing what is still a sensitive species in order to establish breeding but this bird nests in mostly inaccessible places in any case.

There are strong indications that this species' range is still undergoing expansion.

The three possible breeding records from outside Broadland concerned apparently unmated males discovered in a South Norfolk fen, by a Breckland stream with its banks overgrown with willow-herb and hazel scrub, and about a North Norfolk village pond.

This species is protected in Great Britain at all times by special penalties under Schedule 1, Part I of the Wildlife and Countryside Act, 1981.

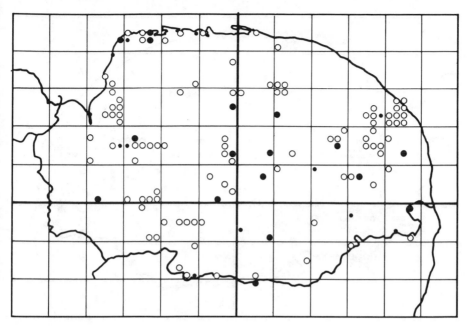

Grasshopper Warbler

Locustella naevia

Tetrads recorded in:	125	(9%)
Possible breeding:	13	(10%)
Probable breeding:	96	(76%)
Confirmed breeding:	17	(13%)

An uncommon summer visitor save in a few favoured localities. This is a bird which tends to skulk among low and tangled vegetation, so it may have been overlooked unless observers heard its distinctive, reeling song. Its overall scarcity is particularly demonstrated by the fact that only in a single instance was breeding proved in adjacent tetrads — TF74N and T, at Brancaster.

This bird occurs in both wet and dry habitats. Its stronghold is among the damp alder carrs, and marshland with sedge, reed and (in slightly drier situations) meadow-sweet, in northern Broadland. It also favours dry heathland and young conifer plantations — most of the records from the west of the county having been made in such sites.

Clearly, this is a species which is particularly vulnerable when its preferred habitats are lost through land reclamation. Its fortunes within the county deserve to be carefully monitored in future.

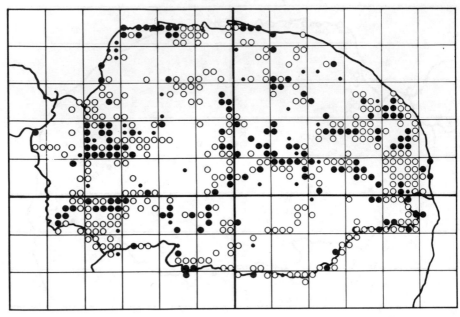

Sedge Warbler

Acrocephalus schoenobaenus

Tetrads recorded in:	499	(34%)
Possible breeding:	38	(8%)
Probable breeding:	301	(60%)
Confirmed breeding:	160	(32%)

A familiar summer visitor, its distribution map picking out in particular the main river systems of the county. In addition, its range will be seen to compare closely with that of the Reed Bunting. Other habitats much frequented by Sedge Warblers include coastal marshes, the peat Fens and Broadland in general. This bird is less inclined to favour wetlands where the common reed is predominant and Reed Warblers are more likely to occur; it can be expected, though, wherever there is coarse, thick vegetation near water. In addition, this species was found by observers in small numbers in certain drier habitats: some albeit damp, such as dried-out ponds with a tangle of brambles about their margins, but in a few cases young coniferous plantations in Breckland.

The song flight of this bird gave rise to most of the records of probable breeding, and should relate to successful nesting within its main range. Sedge Warblers also sing from cover, and in those instances not all observers felt capable of differentiating its notes from those of the Reed Warbler. Most records of possible breeding relate to birds which sang early in the season, then became silent.

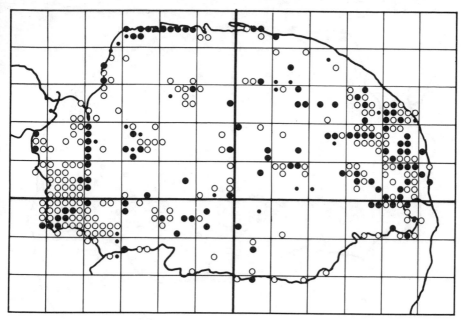

Reed Warbler

Acrocephalus scirpaceus

Tetrads recorded in:	337	*(23%)*
Possible breeding:	23	(7%)
Probable breeding:	200	(60%)
Confirmed breeding:	114	(34%)

Once this species had settled into its favoured habitat as suggested by its own name in the first half of May — it is one of Norfolk's later summer visitors — NBBS workers could visit stands of the common reed and be fairly confident of hearing its song. Many such stands in the Fens — especially the peat Fens — are no wider than the ditches and drains which contain them, but the presence of this bird there was still very evident to the ears of observers passing by on foot or on bicycle. The larger reed-beds of the Ouse Washes, the coast of North Norfolk, and the Broads not surprisingly held the highest numbers and with more birds more records of proven breeding were forthcoming.

Outside the main range of this species, the scatter of records on the map still relate to isolated or discontinuous stretches of *Phragmites*. In such areas in particular, a few Reed Warblers were also noted in other vegetation in or near water with suitable stems to support their nests; for instance, one pair bred in a clump of bamboo in a damp garden near the Bure at Brampton (tetrad TG22L).

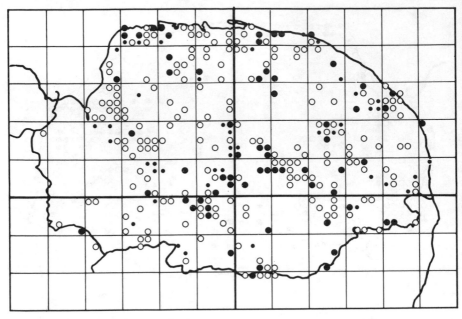

Lesser Whitethroat

Sylvia curruca

Tetrads recorded in:	296	(20%)
Possible breeding:	43	(15%)
Probable breeding:	188	(64%)
Confirmed breeding:	65	(22%)

The least well represented of the county's breeding *Sylvia* warblers, this summer visitor is all the same not a particularly uncommon bird and would appear to have been somewhat under-recorded. There are three apparent reasons for believing this: first, it is species with skulking habits; second, it does not have a song-flight; and third, there is a suspicion that a minority of birdwatchers have never really familiarised themselves with its field characteristics or song. Still, when seen in good light, it is an attractively marked little bird. Furthermore, its rattling song once memorised may be identified with ease.

It is well known that this species did not suffer the 'crash' of 1969 as did its close relative the Whitethroat, for its migratory path took it well to the east of that African drought zone, the Sahel. It shares the Whitethroats liking for hedgerows, but prefers them to be taller and denser. The map shows some correlation with those parts of Norfolk where such hedges as well as marginal land have tended to survive much of the advance of late 20th century intensive farming methods; conversely, many tetrads with suitable habitat and surveyed by workers known to be familiar with this species lacked them.

Like other birds with a liking for thick cover, the open landscapes of Broadland and the Fens hold little attraction for this species. As it happened, the only record of confirmed breeding in the latter area came from a hedge by the busy A10 road in the Cambridgeshire part of a tetrad overlapping the Norfolk boundary (TL59Z).

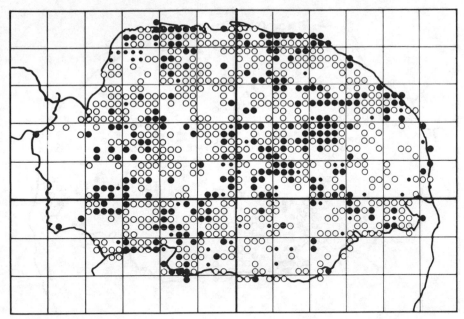

Whitethroat

Sylvia communis

Tetrads recorded in:	781	(54%)
Possible breeding:	53	(7%)
Probable breeding:	488	(62%)
Confirmed breeding:	240	(31%)

Still a widespread summer visitor, despite the 'crash' of 1969 brought about by the drought in its African wintering quarters. Hitherto, this bird had been as common throughout the larger part of Norfolk as the Willow Warbler which has since been the most numerous breeding migrant by far. Whitethroat numbers were regarded as showing something of a recovery during the NBBS period, although a pre-1969 tetrad map would still have shown fewer gaps (save in the most open countryside) than the one given here. A few birds may have been missed by observers due to their relative scarcity in areas with only a small amount of suitable habitat.

The song of the male is often uttered in flight, so probable breeding status was easy to establish. This species frequents scrubland, bramble patches and hedgerows, but generally within more open situations than the other *Sylvia* warblers.

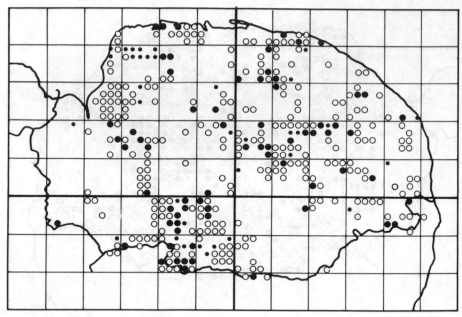

Garden Warbler

Sylvia borin

Tetrads recorded in:	365	(25%)
Possible breeding:	35	(10%)
Probable breeding:	261	(72%)
Confirmed breeding:	69	(19%)

This summer visitor has a scattered range, one which for the most part reflects its preference for dense scrubland, mature deciduous woodland with a thick ground layer of such plants as brambles, and young coniferous plantations. Thus this bird is well represented in Breckland — from whence came many confirmed breeding records — and in the belt of well-wooded country interspersed with heathland extending north-north-westwards from there towards Hunstanton. Other centres of its distribution were chalk scrubland with parkland plantations between Brancaster and Wells-next-the-Sea, plus the Cromer-Holt ridge, parts of Broadland, and areas of woodland and scrub north and west of Norwich.

The lack of Garden Warblers in apparently suitable woodland in the south of the county, for example at Hedenham, Earsham and Redenhall, seems surprising.

This bird has a fine song, but one which can be confused with that of the Blackcap so observers were advised to appraise non-sight records carefully.

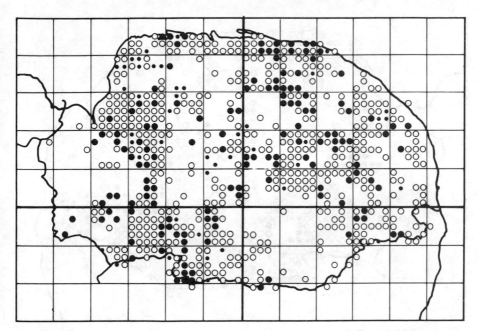

Blackcap

Sylvia atricapilla

Tetrads recorded in:	649	(45%)
Possible breeding:	45	(7%)
Probable breeding:	461	(71%)
Confirmed breeding:	143	(22%)

A fairly common summer visitor — indeed a few (from Northern Europe) have tended to winter in the county over the last twenty years — which observers expect to record during the first half of April. It shares some of the habitat preferences of the closely related Garden Warbler, but is somewhat more widespread. It likes mature deciduous woodland offering plenty of shade, and also frequents thickets and the overgrown surrounds of worked-out gravel pits. Indeed, it is not averse to damper wooded areas, being well-represented in Broadland and in stands of poplars in the Fens.

Open land, such as the Broadland levels and throughout the larger part of the Fens, generally lacks this species. Intensively farmed districts tend to have but few, and there is a suspicion that the occasional pair may have nested in the triangular tract of country lying between Diss, Wymondham and Harleston, where some suitable habitat exists but was missed by NBBS workers.

Given that this is not a scarce bird overall, it may be assumed with confidence that most records of probable breeding would have concerned actual nesting.

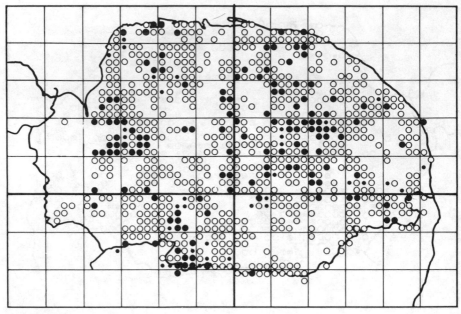

Chiffchaff

Phylloscopus collybita

Tetrads recorded in:	758	(52%)
Possible breeding:	35	(5%)
Probable breeding:	588	(78%)
Confirmed breeding:	135	(18%)

The unmistakable song of the Chiffchaff, reflected in its own name, catches the attention of most Norfolk birdwatchers at some time during the second half of March. Some early songsters are merely pausing during their migratory journey, but with the arrival of April NBBS workers were usually justified in according territorial status to persistently singing birds.

The Chiffchaff's habitat requirements are more exacting than those of the closely related Willow Warbler: standard trees for song-posts and dense undergrowth in which to nest. Observers found it harder to confirm breeding for this species than for the other common warblers, but most singing birds in suitable habitats should have bred successfully.

Although not scarce, this bird was found in but little more than one-half of the tetrads in the county. It was found to avoid most of the Fens — the Ouse Washes excepted — and open areas of Broadland, as well as intensively-farmed tracts of country.

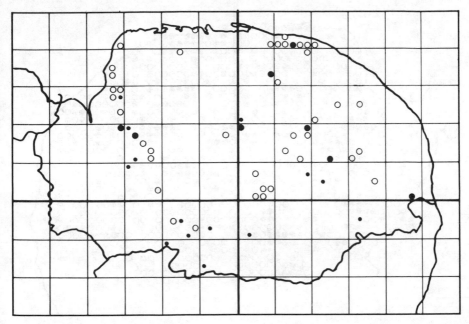

Wood Warbler

Phylloscopus sibilatrix

Tetrads recorded in:	62	(4%)
Possible breeding:	14	(23%)
Probable breeding:	40	(65%)
Confirmed breeding:	8	(13%)

An uncommon summer visitor to beech, birch, oak and sweet chestnut woods (including stands of these trees in park-type country) with little undergrowth. Seago, writing in 1967 (*Birds of Norfolk*), described this bird as local, scarce and decreasing; however, the BTO/IWC *Atlas* project of 1968-1972 seemed to indicate that the decrease in range had been arrested, while the NBBS has shown a clear increase in this attractive songster's range. Data from these two surveys, in respect of 10-km squares *not* tetrads, may be presented as follows:

1968- 1972		1980-1985
3	Possible breeding	8
6	Probable breeding	15
7	Confirmed breeding	8
16	10-km squares found in	31

The well-timbered hinterland of Sheringham is an established stronghold of this species, but there does appear to have been a re-colonisation of certain sites along the greensand belt of West Norfolk which were deserted in the 1950s and 1960s. Most of the other records came from the well-wooded country about Norwich, while a pocket of suitable habitat apparently exists about Kimberley and Wicklewood. A few records were submitted from Breckland tetrads, although this species never seems to have been common there.

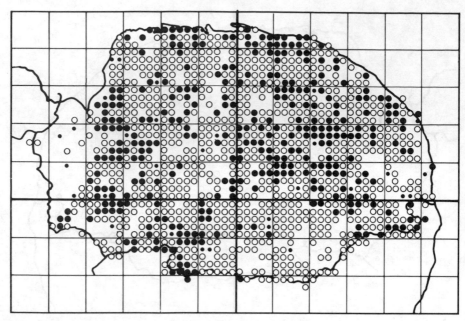

Willow Warbler

Phylloscopus trochilus

Tetrads recorded in:	1,117	(77%)
Possible breeding:	30	(3%)
Probable breeding:	753	(67%)
Confirmed breeding:	334	(30%)

Although less widespread than the Turtle Dove, Swallow and House Martin, the Willow Warbler is our most common Summer visitor. Its easily recognisable song is usually heard somewhere in Norfolk by the end of the first week in April, and by the end of this month most birds are holding territory.

Similar in appearance to its close relative the Chiffchaff, the Willow Warbler occurs in a far wider range of habitats. It sings for the most part from bushes or small trees, and nests in long grass or other vegetation within the immediate vicinity of its song-posts. Thus young coniferous plantations, open woodland, Broadland carrs, the thorn and sallow thickets of the Ouse Washes, and most marginal land were all found to hold good numbers of singing, if not definitely breeding, birds. Breeding, established in 30% of the tetrads, was usually confirmed by seeing the adults carrying food to their young or through observing attendant fledglings.

Open country, certain coastal sites, and the most densely built-up parts of towns accounted for most of the tetrads in which this species was not recorded.

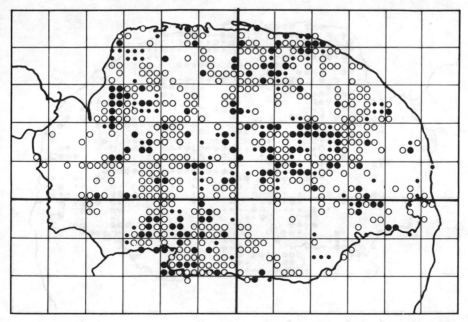

Goldcrest

Regulus regulus

Tetrads recorded in:	588	(40%)
Possible breeding:	84	(14%)
Probable breeding:	363	(62%)
Confirmed breeding:	141	(24%)

A common bird in its preferred habitat of coniferous woodland, including small and isolated plantations. It was found in 4% more Norfolk tetrads than the Coal Tit, although the overall range of these two species was found to be similar. The Goldcrest was, however, proved to breed in fewer instances than the Coal Tit; it can hardly be a less familiar bird, but its nest and attendant young were not so easily located within the thick cover of many plantations. The Goldcrest's distinctive calls were readily noted, and virtually all records of probable breeding are likely to have related to successful nesting.

Away from plantations, this bird was also observed in large gardens and church-yards containing evergreen trees and shrubs.

A few pairs were located in oakwoods, and one pair with young were found in an isolated hedgerow oak at Wellingham (tetrad TF82T).

The scatter of probable breeding records in the Fens and Broadland indicate that this species will colonise spots well away from its main range if it can find a suitable nesting location.

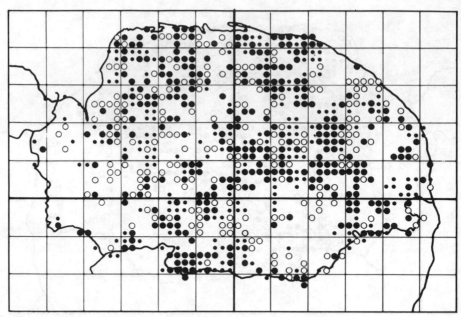

Spotted Flycatcher

Muscicapa striata

Tetrads recorded in:	683	(47%)
Possible breeding:	177	(26%)
Probable breeding:	194	(28%)
Confirmed breeding:	312	(46%)

One of our latest summer visitors, the Spotted Flycatcher does not often establish its territory until mid-May. This little bird does not have a striking appearance, but its acrobatic forays after its insect prey should not have been missed by NBBS workers. This species frequents woodland margins, parklands and park-type country, churchyards and large gardens. It was not recorded in quite extensive tracts of countryside where some occurrences might have been expected; yet, where a species such as this is not especially numerous (although by no means uncommon), it is of course possible that some birds were overlooked. On the other hand, B.D. Harding noted in his *Bedfordshire Bird Atlas* (1979) that similar pockets of absence occurred there.

This bird did occur in Broadland and to a lesser extent Fenland; most records from those parts were focussed upon the villages, but patches of willows, or isolated and sometimes abandoned gardens with over-mature fruit trees, yielded results on occasion.

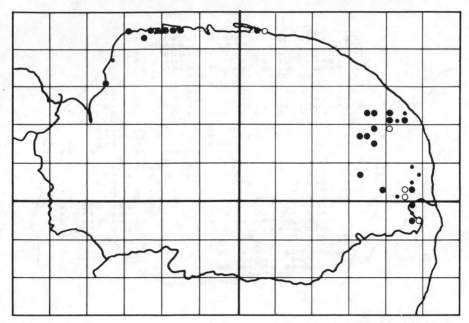

Bearded Tit

Panurus biarmicus

Tetrads recorded in:	38	*(3%)*
Possible breeding:	8	(21%)
Probable breeding:	5	(13%)
Confirmed breeding:	25	(66%)

Following consultation with conservation bodies and other interested parties, it was decided to omit records of confirmed breeding in two West Norfolk tetrads from the above map.

This species was almost driven to extinction by the late 19th century, due to the activities of collectors and trappers as much as through the drainage of many of its wetland habitats, and the Norfolk Broads were to provide one of its last remaining strongholds in England. Conservation schemes and legislation, both prompted by and prompting a more enlightened public attitude, have together ensured the recovery of this most attractive resident bird — although it remains at risk during winters when heavy snow blankets the reed-beds to which it resorts almost exclusively. Mercifully, while there were three winters with periods of severe frosts during the NBBS, heavy snowfall was infrequent in the county. The NBBS has been able to show that Norfolk, with its extensive reed-beds, remains of national significance for this bird — the number of breeding pairs varying between 200 and 300 during this project.

This species is protected in Great Britain at all times by special penalties under Schedule 1, Part I of the Wildlife and Countryside Act, 1981.

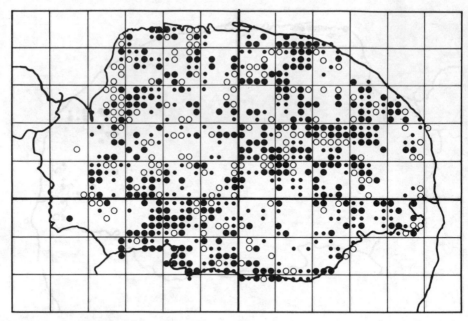

Long-tailed Tit

Aegithalos caudatus

Tetrads recorded in:	672	(46%)
Possible breeding:	217	(32%)
Probable breeding:	151	(22%)
Confirmed breeding:	304	(45%)

A familiar and attractive resident of woodland margins, overgrown hedgerows and scrub — including chalk downland scrub — which ought not to have been missed by observers. A few occurrences may have gone unrecorded in respect of, say, isolated overgrown marl-pits which could not readily be approached without trampling crops. The distinctive, ball-shaped nest of this species tends to survive the dying down of surrounding vegetation in autumn, and breeding was proved in several tetrads through such used nests being found. Family parties were the most common sightings that proved nesting.

Long-tailed Tits do not nest in heavily built-up locations (although small flocks have often been observed passing from tree to tree in the centre of Norwich in winter). Prairie-type farmland produced few records, although it came as a surprise that suitable thorn hedges on the claylands of South Norfolk did not yield many Long-tailed Tits — Magpies were common there, though, and may well predate upon these tiny birds. Long-tailed Tits were all but absent from Fenland and open country in Broadland; the map shows that their breeding distribution stops abruptly at the edges of these flatlands.

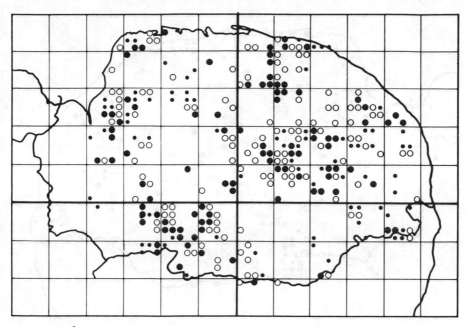

Marsh Tit

Parus palustris

Tetrads recorded in:	304	(21%)
Possible breeding:	78	(26%)
Probable breeding:	127	(42%)
Confirmed breeding:	99	(33%)

This resident is not uncommon in many areas; however, regarding the above map, it is to be hoped that data submitted by NBBS workers was not subject to any confusion with the somewhat similar Willow Tit. Calls, were they heard, should have provided satisfactory evidence for differentiating between these two species.

The Marsh Tit's own name is misleading, for it is not a marshland bird but rather one which frequents deciduous woodland or at least well-wooded countryside. All the same, some were found in drier wooded localities within Broadland. It was found to be most prevalent in the hinterland of Norwich, in Breckland, the well-timbered lower Cretaceous country to the north-east of King's Lynn, and about the Cromer-Holt ridge and the upper Bure. It may well have been overlooked in ostensibly suitable woodland on the claylands of South Norfolk.

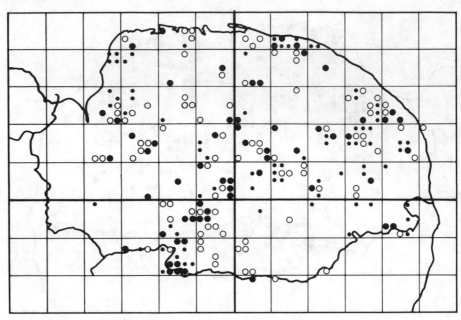

Willow Tit

Parus montanus

Tetrads recorded in:	226	(16%)
Possible breeding:	75	(33%)
Probable breeding:	89	(39%)
Confirmed breeding:	62	(27%)

A distinctly local resident, which it is hoped that few if any NBBS workers would have confused with the similar Marsh Tit — the latter being the more widespread of the two species. The Willow Tit's name is also misleading, for it has no clear preference for frequenting willows of any kind. On the other hand it excavates its nest holes in these trees or in the alders, birches and elders which grow in the damp locations it favours, although not exclusively. Thus, in Breckland it was found among deciduous trees planted about the margins of some coniferous plantations on the dry expanse of Thetford Warren, as well as in the damp thickets about Sturston and Thompson.

This species was not identified in the county until 1893 and was not proved to breed here until 1934. In more than one-half of the tetrads in which it was found during the NBBS — 129 or 57% — the Marsh Tit was also located, illustrating a fair degree of range overlap. It is hoped that the data which has been submitted in respect of these two birds will aid future detailed investigation of their habitat requirements.

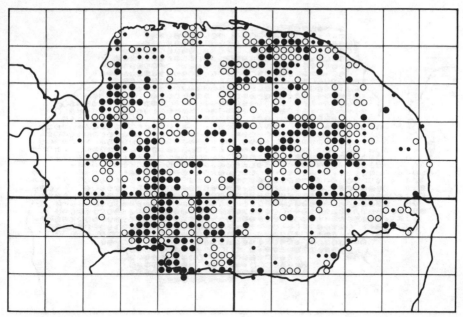

Coal Tit

Parus ater

Tetrads recorded in:	*524*	*(36%)*
Possible breeding:	129	(25%)
Probable breeding:	189	(36%)
Confirmed breeding:	206	(39%)

Breeding Coal Tits are concentrated upon areas of coniferous woodland, or at least woods and well-wooded districts with a sizeable proportion of preferably mature conifers. Churchyards and large gardens often fall within this last habitat group; but some NBBS workers found this species at low densities in oak woodland with either a scatter of conifers or none at all. Outside the breeding season, this bird ranges more widely and is not unfamiliar at bird-tables.

There was no complete 10-km square where this species was not found, although hardly any were located in the Fens and Broadland. Blocks of contiguous tetrads with confirmed breeding indicate the areas where the highest numbers of Coal Tits were found; certainly a species which has benefitted from the afforestation programmes of the present century. Its range will be seen to compare well with that of the Goldcrest.

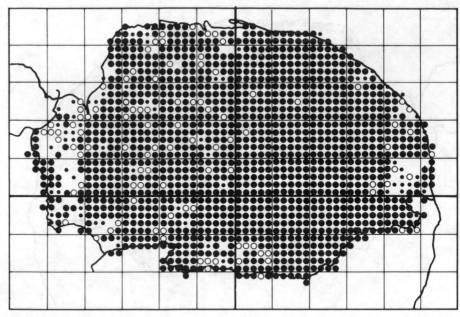

Blue Tit

Parus caeruleus

Tetrads recorded in:	1,356	(93%)
Possible breeding:	65	(5%)
Probable breeding:	98	(7%)
Confirmed breeding:	1,193	(88%)

There can be no one who is not familiar with this common and widespread bird, yet it was found in only the tenth highest number of tetrads. The latter point has to be qualified by the statement that only a few tetrads separated the relative positions of most of the more common breeding species.

The only parts of the county where there were contiguous tetrads without breeding season records were saltings and exposed sections of the coast, and sections of Halvergate Levels and the Fens. The Blue Tit is found in all Fenland towns and villages, however, and only avoids the most open tracts of land there. Indeed, both in the Fens and on Halvergate Levels, this bird occurs about isolated cottages and farm-steads, including abandoned ones, where there are at least a few bushes. All non-proven records, save for some of the possible ones on the very edge of this bird's range, doubtless concerned Blue Tits which actually nested.

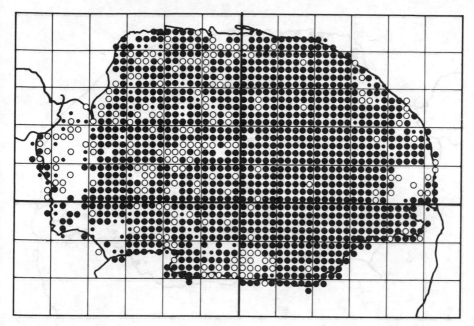

Great Tit

Parus major

Tetrads recorded in:	1,309	(90%)
Possible breeding:	72	(6%)
Probable breeding:	187	(14%)
Confirmed breeding:	1,050	(80%)

This bold and familiar bird is one which no NBBS observer could have missed. Throughout its extensive range, it is almost always less abundant than the Blue Tit; and, while the former was just as easily recorded in most tetrads, the fact that it was only recorded as singing or holding territory in rather more squares than the latter — usually in areas of open farmland — points in particular to a somewhat smaller population.

Having made this point, the loud and distinctive calls and song announcing the establishment of territories by late winter led to the precise range of this bird being mapped. It was generally absent from the same coastal, Broadland and Fenland tetrads as the Blue Tit, but more markedly so in those districts.

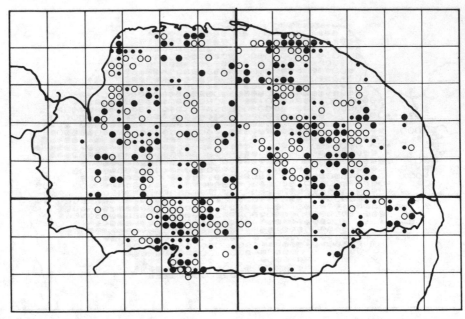

Nuthatch

Sitta europaea

Tetrads recorded in:	389	(27%)
Possible breeding:	121	(31%)
Probable breeding:	149	(38%)
Confirmed breeding:	119	(31%)

This resident is not uncommon, although any birdwatcher who does not move far from his or her home patch may well be unfamiliar with it as there are wide tracts of the county in which few if any are recorded. It shares a liking for deciduous woodland and parkland with the Treecreeper, but is less usual once coniferous trees make up the larger component of any block or group of standing timber. This bird was found to be most widespread about Breckland and in the well-wooded band of country extending north-north-west from there towards Hunstanton, in well-timbered countryside surrounding Norwich, and about the Cromer-Holt ridge. Elsewhere, smaller groups of tetrads with Nuthatches contain landscaped parks such as Holkham,

Raynham, Sennowe and Lexham.

Some observers discovered the unmistakable, mud-rendered hole nest of this species; however, even if it were not proved to breed, lower categories are still likely to have related to the nesting of this essentially sedentary bird.

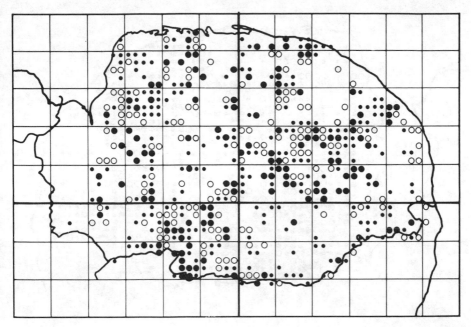

Treecreeper

Certhia familiaris

Tetrads recorded in:	498	(34%)
Possible breeding:	213	(43%)
Probable breeding:	149	(30%)
Confirmed breeding:	136	(27%)

A widespread resident, occurring in just over one-third of all tetrads. This species, unmistakable in both appearance and behaviour, is found in both deciduous woodland, especially where oaks are dominant, and mixed plantations, especially those containing Scots pine and exotic trees. Other locations in which Treecreepers may be met with include parkland, churchyards and long-established cemeteries; also large gardens.

Most Treecreepers nest behind flaps of bark or within fissures on tree trunks, although sometimes crevices in wooden huts or similar structures are utilised. Like the Nuthatch, which shares much of the same kind of habitat, this is a sedentary species and even possible breeding records are likely to concern breeding pairs. Indeed, the higher proportion of possible breeding records submitted for this bird may seem a trifle puzzling; however, a subjective impression which may explain this is that more Treecreepers than Nuthatches are seen singly as opposed to in pairs.

Virtual absence from obvious tracts of open land is only to be expected for a bird of this kind, although a few were noted by NBBS workers along hedgerows well away from woodland proper provided they contained mature oaks.

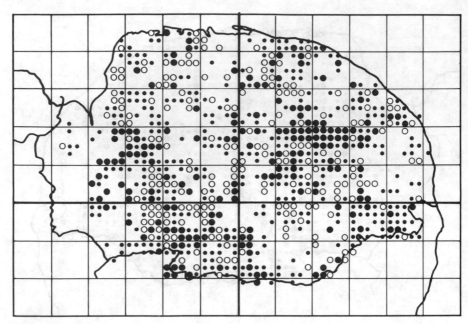

Jay

Garrulus glandarius

Tetrads recorded in:	732	(50%)
Possible breeding:	345	(47%)
Probable breeding:	201	(27%)
Confirmed breeding:	186	(25%)

The most widespread resident crow, Jays were found in one-half of Norfolk's tetrads. Conversely, the percentage of those in which breeding was confirmed was the lowest for the crow family — this latter feature paralleled in the comparable Bedfordshire and Kent projects (see bibliography). This doubtless results from the Jay's liking for deep cover in woodland for nesting purposes; and not all woods could be searched systematically by NBBS workers, either through restrictions being placed upon their visits or through mere lack of time. Woods which *were* checked thoroughly in each year the Survey lasted, especially those from Belaugh west through Horsford and Felthorpe to Lenwade, resulted in high concentrations of proved breeding records. Vir-

tually all tetrads with probable breeding, and many of those with possible breeding, would have contained nesting Jays.

The Jay has remained plentiful throughout the wooded districts of Norfolk, despite game preservation. Breeding was confirmed in the well-keepered Wroxham area — compare Magpie and Carrion Crow. Jays are quite content to breed in extensive coniferous plantations, such as Thetford Warren, where other crows were found to be scarce or absent.

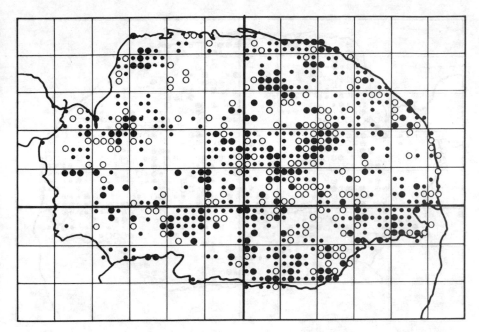

Magpie

Pica pica

Tetrads recorded in:	623	(43%)
Possible breeding:	308	(49%)
Probable breeding:	153	(25%)
Confirmed breeding:	162	(26%)

The population of Magpies has continued to rise since they enjoyed something of a respite from the predations of gamekeepers during the First World War. In addition, many were to be driven from their Breckland stronghold by the subsequent afforestation programme, followed by clearance of blackthorn from the 'Battle Area' established in the Second World War. The spread of this attractive and even entertaining bird has been a mixed blessing, for in areas where they are concentrated they take the eggs and fledglings of many a songbird in spring.

Breeding Magpies are attracted by high, unkempt hedgerows, overgrown marlpits, thickets and marginal land in general. Their used nests are distinctive, and could be pick-ed out even from a speeding train to add to the relevant tetrad recording card. Apart from areas where this bird is prevented from establishing itself as a resident by keepers, for instance in the Wroxham district, it was found to be scarce or absent in dense Breckland plantations, in much of the Broads and Fens regions, and from the 'well-manicured' farmland of west-central and north-west Norfolk.

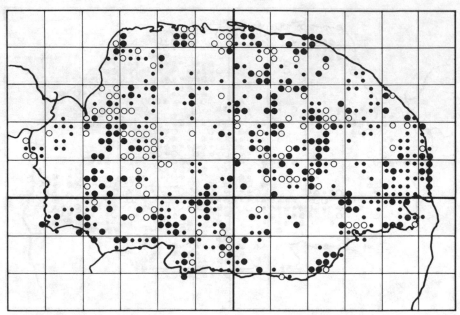

Jackdaw

Corvus monedula

Tetrads recorded in:	524	(36%)
Possible breeding:	240	(46%)
Probable breeding:	105	(20%)
Confirmed breeding:	179	(34%)

This is a species which many ornithologists have blandly assumed is both common and widespread, yet it has taken a scientifically organised project like the NBBS to show that this is not so in many parts of the county. Indeed, a scattered range is revealed, with certain areas having concentrations of Jackdaws separated by tracts of country with few if any of these birds.

Jackdaws often associate with Rooks, yet they were only proved to breed in one tetrad in the 10-km square, TM19, which had the highest total of those with rookeries. It is often associated with urban areas, and while this is particularly noticeable in respect of Great Yarmouth it was not recorded in all the tetrads of Greater Norwich. Wells-next-the-Sea had none, although this bird bred or probably bred throughout the extensive parkland of nearby Holkham. Other parks, or park-type habitats such as those in and about Breckland, also held breeding colonies.

Many records of probable breeding relate to birds spotted in the vicinity of likely nesting sites which they were not seen to enter. Records of presence in Broadland often relate to wandering birds, although some nests in isolated drainage mills and derelict farm buildings may have been overlooked.

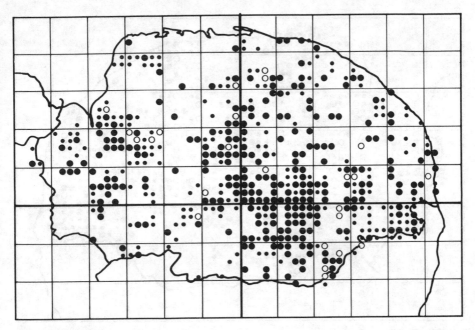

Rook

Corvus frugilegus

Tetrads recorded in:	483	(33%)
Possible breeding:	187	(39%)
Probable breeding:	24	(5%)
Confirmed breeding:	272	(56%)

It might come as a mild shock to many naturalists that this familiar resident was found to be the least widespread member of the crow family. On the other hand, it was proved to breed in a higher number of tetrads than its relatives: this not surprising in view of the often readily apparent siting of most rookeries. No specific survey of these was undertaken during the NBBS period; however, it is interesting to note a quite close correlation between the boulder-clay region of South and Central Norfolk — the wood-pasture zone of landscape historians — and the area having the greatest number of rookeries. This apparent link deserves further investigation.

It may be hard to accept that rookeries, which were often spotted in winter to give confirmed breeding records, could be missed by observers; however, some small ones may well have been missed in tetrads which were not covered until most trees had acquired full leaf cover in late spring. Some of these are certain to have existed in tetrads from which possible or probable breeding records were forthcoming.

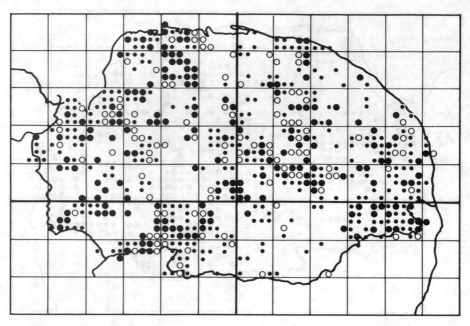

Carrion Crow

Corvus corone

Tetrads recorded in:	*581*	*(40%)*
Possible breeding:	292	(50%)
Probable breeding:	106	(18%)
Confirmed breeding:	183	(31%)

A widespread resident, recorded in every complete 10-km square. Broadland and Breckland have long been recognised as strongholds of this species; but, as it was not always easy to gain access to likely nesting sites in those parts, many probable and possible records there doubtless related to breeding pairs. The upper reaches of rivers draining into Broadland (although not the Waveney), the well-wooded tracts of country between Norwich and Cromer and to the north-east of King's Lynn, north-west Norfolk, the silt Fens, the lower Wissey and the Ouse Washes all have concentrations of these birds.

The activities of keepers are known to account for gaps in the Carrion Crow's range about the Cressinghams, the Barshams and Wroxham. Absence from Stow Bardolph and Methwold Fens doubtless relates to a shortage of suitable nesting sites; near absence from the heavy claylands south of a line from Wymondham to Brooke down to the county boundary is puzzling, for there are suitable woodlands and other sites here and few keepered estates.

118

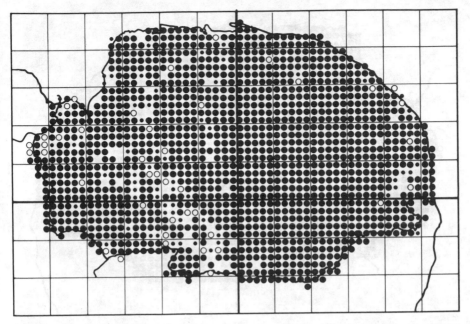

Starling

Sturnus vulgaris

Tetrads recorded in:	1,387	(95%)
Possible breeding:	72	(5%)
Probable breeding:	41	(3%)
Confirmed breeding:	1,274	(92%)

NBBS workers could hardly have overlooked this bold and assertive species, so the map should depict its range with particular accuracy. The above figures indicate that the Starling was found to be the fifth most widespread breeding bird, with nesting having been confirmed in the third highest number of tetrads.

Areas where Starlings were not recorded — or only given possible breeding status — were mostly restricted to the coast, to open farmland, marsh, and to extensive stretches of coniferous plantations. Buildings in the 'Battle Area' were almost always too disturbed for the likes of either Starlings or House Sparrows; sufficient Starlings thereabouts were found to exploit holes in trees to prevent this species from exhibiting

the striking range gap which can be seen on the House Sparrow map.

The presence of breeding Starlings may occasionally be a nuisance or even a health hazard; whatever the relative level of the love-hate feelings which most of us have for this bird, we may all be thankful that it does not nest in winter when Norfolk experiences influxes of giant flocks from the Continent!

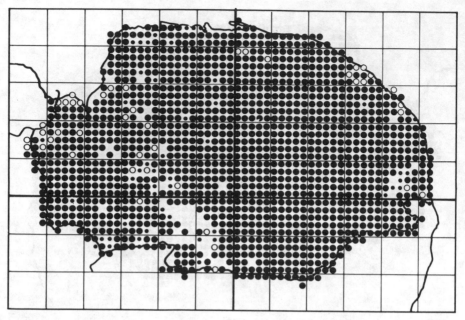

House Sparrow

Passer domesticus

Tetrads recorded in:	1,377	(95%)
Possible breeding:	54	(4%)
Probable breeding:	42	(3%)
Confirmed breeding:	1,281	(93%)

This, the bird most likely to be taken for granted by observers, was in fact only the eighth most widespread species in the NBBS. Areas of total absence turned out to be the following: coastal squares with habitats limited to saltings, shingle, cliffs and cliff-top pasture; open farmland; forest; and, surprisingly in some instances, much of the Breckland 'Battle Area'.

In respect of records of confirmed breeding, the House Sparrow was only beaten into second place by the Blackbird. The distinctive nests of the House Sparrow were among those which could be picked out at any time, whether or not they were occupied; furthermore, the ostentatiously importunate newly fledged young could hardly have been missed in most cases.

While they are generally commensal with man, disturbance by the military and a lack of food in the depopulated 'Battle Area' would seem to provide reasons why they have not colonised otherwise attractive sites there.

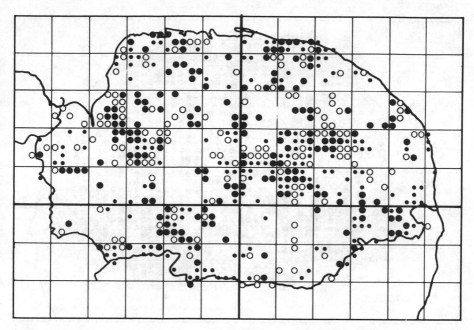

Tree Sparrow

Passer montanus

Tetrads recorded in:	527	*(36%)*
Possible breeding:	212	(40%)
Probable breeding:	140	(27%)
Confirmed breeding:	175	(33%)

Tree Sparrows were recorded in just over one-third of all Norfolk tetrads. This species can be retiring, although inconspicuous might be a better description, so some were doubtless missed by observers; on the other hand, the Tree Sparrow is known to avoid apparently suitable breeding locations for a succession of seasons, before re-establishing a colony.

There is no complete 10-km square in which no Tree Sparrows were found. Tetrads which were worked exhaustively usually had records of at least presence, although this was by no means always the case. Where squares were visited only once or on but a few occasions, familiarity with this bird's calls helped many observers to locate the species.

On balance, then, the patchy range of the Tree Sparrow relates to its general standing. Absence from much of the Peat Fens of the far south-west may have been due to the removal of pollared willows which were once widespread there.

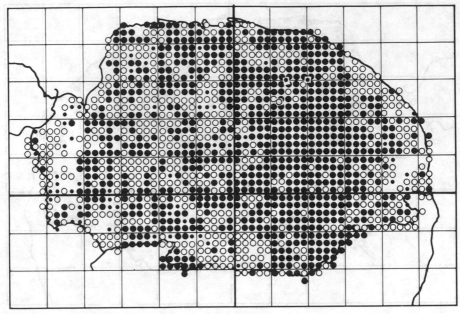

Chaffinch

Fringilla coelebs

Tetrads recorded in:	1,350	(93%)
Possible breeding:	59	(4%)
Probable breeding:	528	(39%)
Confirmed breeding:	763	(57%)

The status of the Chaffinch as the most widespread breeding finch in the county was confirmed by the NBBS. While comprehensive numerical data was not assembled, this was the only finch for which breeding was proved in over half of the tetrads in which it was recorded. The Chaffinch was clearly the most common finch over the larger part of its range, although the Greenfinch was more numerous in most gardens and urban parks for instance.

Even where this bird was markedly scarce, it is likely that records of possible and probable breeding meant that nesting almost certainly occurred at some time during the Survey period. Absence from the treeless expanse of Halvergate Levels and from certain coastal squares did not come as

a surprise, although some blank tetrads in the Fens did have limited areas which this species might exploit from time to time. Few if any recorders could have been unfamiliar with its cheerful, rattling song, so this bird's range as mapped here can be regarded as very close to accurate.

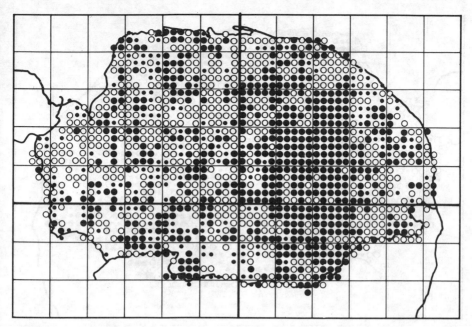

Greenfinch

Carduelis chloris

Tetrads recorded in:	1,251	(86%)
Possible breeding:	161	(13%)
Probable breeding:	557	(44%)
Confirmed breeding:	553	(44%)

A common and widespread bird, with the densest breeding population concentrated in large gardens and shrubberies. In such usually limited areas, this was found to be more common than the Chaffinch, although it was found in about one hundred fewer tetrads overall. As well as being absent in most cases from tetrads which had no Chaffinches, Greenfinches were not found in a number of contiguous squares in central southern Norfolk; these tended to have a concentration of unfavourable habitats — dense coniferous plantations, open heathland and prairie farmland.

The distinctive *dwee* call of a Greenfinch is one of the first that a young birdwatcher learns; records of probable breeding derived from hearing this species call persistently doubtless related in every instance to proved nesting. One bar to proving breeding with the Greenfinch is that adults often carry food to their young in a less conspicuous way than most birds.

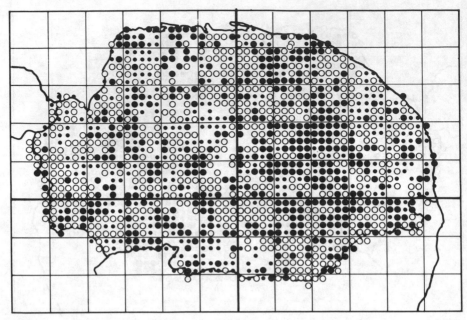

Goldfinch

Carduelis carduelis

Tetrads recorded in:	1,249	(86%)
Possible breeding:	257	(21%)
Probable breeding:	567	(45%)
Confirmed breeding:	425	(34%)

The Goldfinch was found to occur in almost the same number of tetrads as its close relative the Greenfinch, but it was proved to breed in as many as ten per cent fewer squares. There would appear to be no observational reasons which render the Goldfinch's breeding harder to prove, so it is clearly the less common of the two species over the larger part of their shared range. A comparison of the maps does, however, show that Goldfinches are more widespread than Greenfinches in the peat Fens of southwest Norfolk.

Once hedgerows become stripped of their leaves in late autumn, the distinctive used nests of Goldfinches are often revealed and a number of instances of proved breeding were made in this way. Observers were advised not to record young which, while fully fledged, are marked by their lack of a red face; these birds, which flock from late July and roam areas with seeding plants, soon leave the tetrad they were raised in.

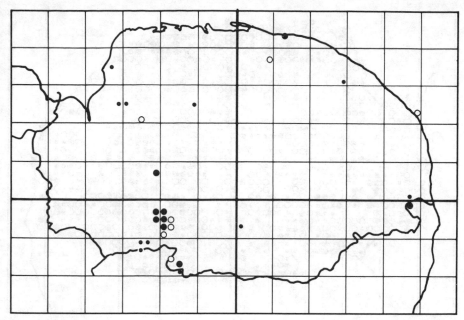

Siskin

Carduelis spinus

Tetrads recorded in:	27	(2%)
Possible breeding:	11	(41%)
Probable breeding:	7	(26%)
Confirmed breeding:	9	(33%)

A relatively new breeding bird for the county, this having been established for the first time in 1961 when an adult pair with fully fledged young were seen at Ringland. While this species is mostly observed in winter among alders and birches, it nests in coniferous woodland with spruces and pines being particularly favoured. Such plantations are widespread in Breckland, with generally small to medium-sized ones scattered elsewhere, so it is not surprising that a breeding population (which may have been overlooked prior to the 1960s) has become established.

The map indicates the nine tetrads in which this species definitely bred over the 1980-1985 period. The block of contiguous tetrads in the Mundford-Hilborough district of Breckland was found to have a small, established population of Siskins; the scatter of confirmed records both from other parts of the Brecks and further afield are more likely to represent isolated occurrences. The impression gained from the input of NBBS data was that no more than ten pairs have bred in any one year, although it has to be said that family parties (which provide the most easily gained proof of breeding) may well be overlooked in some cases among extensive plantations.

Most of the records shown which fell short of proved breeding relate to birds which were singing, or were merely seen, in suitable habitat as late as early May, then disappeared.

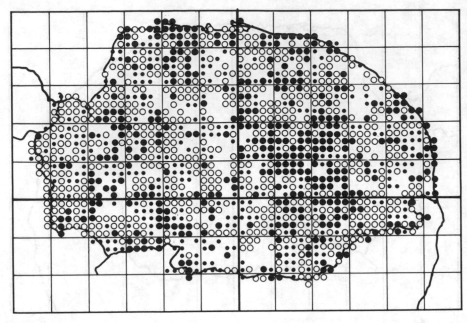

Linnet

Carduelis cannabina

Tetrads recorded in:	1,213	(83%)
Possible breeding:	279	(23%)
Probable breeding:	577	(48%)
Confirmed breeding:	357	(29%)

It may come as a surprise that this clearly common and widespread species was not proved to breed in more tetrads, although most of those in the Fens, for instance, were only visited in the last one or two seasons of the NBBS. Here and elsewhere, the high proportion of probable breeding records must relate in most instances to successful nesting.

The Linnet will exploit lower nesting sites than other finches, and is the only member of this family to breed in the *Sueada* of those Norfolk extremities, Blakeney Point and Scolt Head. Gaps in the Linnet's range, save for the very centre of Norwich, parts of Halvergate Levels, and mature coniferous plantations in Breckland, are not easy to explain; some birds may

have been overlooked by observers, of course, although grubbing up of hedgerows and marginal land in areas of intensive arable farming — in the Fersfield district, for example — has eradicated pockets of nesting Linnets.

126

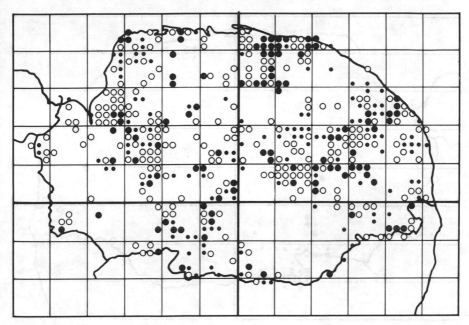

Redpoll

Carduelis flammea

Tetrads recorded in:	447	*(31%)*
Possible breeding:	121	(27%)
Probable breeding:	223	(50%)
Confirmed breeding:	103	(23%)

This might be described as the least common of the common finches; it is widespread where its prefered breeding habitats are extensive, but scarce or absent elsewhere. The map clearly picks out these favoured regions — alder carrs and birch, thorn and willow thickets in Broadland, birch heathland and young forestry plantations. The number of contiguous tetrads with confirmed breeding on the heaths and marginal land of the Cromer-Holt ridge, surveyed independently by a number of observers, indicates a particularly high concentration of this species. The band of country extending north-north-west from Breckland to the hinterland of Hunstanton is similarly attractive to this bird.

Redpolls will nest in farmland away from their strongholds where marginal habitats have been retained but only in small numbers. Thus it is likely that their overall scarcity in such areas has meant that some occurrences were overlooked by NBBS workers. The discontinuity of expanses of their favoured nesting sites in the Fens has meant that they are far less common there than in Broadland.

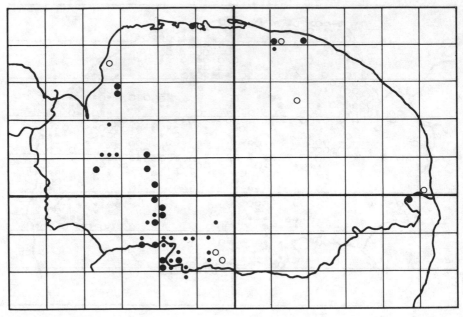

Crossbill

Loxia curvirostra

Tetrads recorded in:	49	(3%)
Possible breeding:	23	(47%)
Probable breeding:	7	(14%)
Confirmed breeding:	19	(39%)

An uncommon and local resident, its numbers periodically reinforced by irruptions from the spruce forests of Northern Europe during late summer and autumn. No marked invasion has occurred since 1966, so the above map indicates the stabilised breeding range of this species. First recorded as having bred in the county in 1829, regular nesting from 1910 came in the train of a major irruption the year before. This is a denizen of spruce and pine woodland, and its foothold in Breckland was turned into a stronghold as a consequence of the inter-war programme of afforestation there. Other localities in which it nests annually or at least frequently include the Waveney Forest of South-east Norfolk (formerly in Suffolk, until the boundary change of 1974), the Cromer-Holt ridge, and the neighbourhood of Wells/Holkham and Sandringham.

Crossbills breed from midwinter through to early spring, so this would have been the bird with which observers could have commenced their annual NBBS recording.

Within Breckland in particular, a number of probable and possible records would almost certainly have related to nesting in plantations with severe access limitations.

This species is protected at all times in Great Britain by special penalties under Schedule 1, Part I of the Wildlife and Countryside Act, 1981.

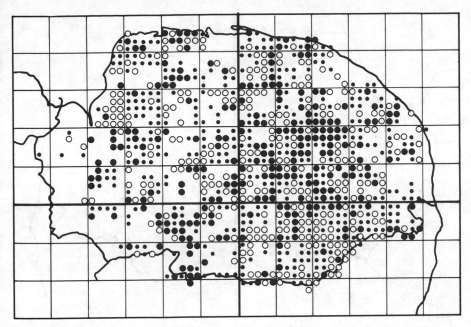

Bullfinch

Pyrrhula pyrrhula

Tetrads recorded in:	870	(60%)
Possible breeding:	336	(39%)
Probable breeding:	286	(33%)
Confirmed breeding:	248	(29%)

A fairly common resident throughout wide tracts of the county, yet scarce or even unknown in certain districts. The range is generally restricted to areas with plenty of thick cover, especially in the form of overgrown hedgerows, heathland thickets and young forestry plantations. The map gives a particularly good impression of districts this bird avoids; open farmland, grazing marshes, and by far the larger part of the Fens. Bullfinches are notorious for their predations on the buds of fruit trees, and are regarded as pests where these are grown commercially. The scatter of records from the Marshland district of the Fens, where there are many such orchards, suggests that a marked colonisation would occur there if there was no persecution.

Bullfinches are immediately recognisable by sight, but while their call-note is distinctive their soft song is not well known; were they more vocal songsters many of the possible breeding records would doubtless have been entered as probables. However, even a brief glimpse of a Bullfinch's white rump as it disappears into cover in spring is likely to mean that nesting is taking place or will take place in that vicinity.

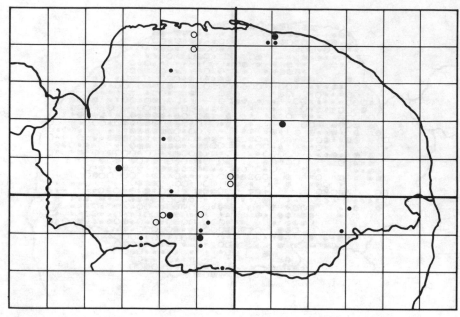

Hawfinch

Coccothraustes coccothraustes

Tetrads recorded in:	26	(2%)
Possible breeding:	13	(50%)
Probable breeding:	7	(27%)
Confirmed breeding:	6	(23%)

One record of confirmed breeding in the TF70 10-km square has not been mapped at the request of the observer concerned.

An uncommon, even rare resident, which is known to breed regularly in but one locality in Norfolk. This site is in Breckland, and as may be seen from the above map most of the instances of its occurrence during the breeding season came from that district. This is a bird of open deciduous woodland and park-type country, and it is most likely to occur when trees which bear fruit with hard seeds — a favoured food — are present. Hornbeams, for instance, are resorted to in at least one Breckland locality.

The Hawfinch is a particularly wary bird, and it is almost certain that a few observers missed seeing birds which were actually present when carrying out their NBBS fieldwork. It is, after all, not a species that birdwatchers expect to see in by far the larger part of the county. It does tend to be sedentary, so at least some of the records of probable breeding are likely to have related to pairs which actually did so.

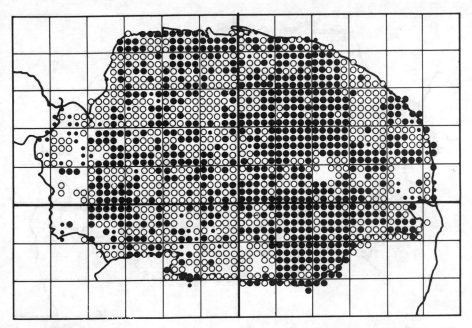

Yellowhammer

Emberiza citrinella

Tetrads recorded in:	1,300	(89%)
Possible breeding:	56	(4%)
Probable breeding:	576	(44%)
Confirmed breeding:	668	(51%)

The Yellowhammer always appears to have been a common breeding species in the larger part of Norfolk. This familiar denizen of farmland, woodland margins, young forestry plantations and heathland has been shown by the NBBS to avoid marshland pasture and certain areas of 'prairie farming' — Halvergate Marshes and the larger part of the peat Fens reflect this absence or at least scarcity, as may be seen on the distribution map. Breeding Yellowhammers also avoid saltings and the inner-urban zone of Norwich.

Most records of probable breeding derive from observers having heard the familiar song of the Yellowhammer; in such instances this species almost certainly bred, yet in areas of overall scarcity such as the Silt Fens possible breeding records may merely relate to passing, unpaired birds.

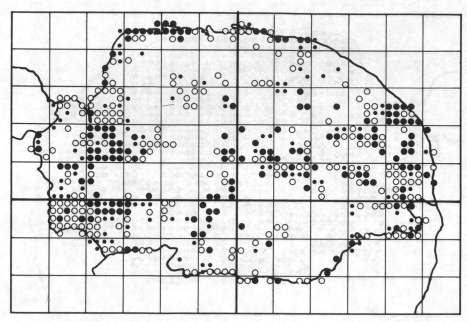

Reed Bunting

Emberiza schoeniclus

Tetrads recorded in:	484	(33%)
Possible breeding:	101	(21%)
Probable breeding:	221	(46%)
Confirmed breeding:	162	(33%)

The breeding range of this bird compares well with that of the Sedge Warbler; there also being a marked coincidence between the tetrads in which breeding was confirmed for both species. Unlike the Reed Warbler, the Reed Bunting is not essentially restricted to areas with beds of the common reed.

This species' main range still relates to the wetlands of the county. It has also chosen to exploit certain other habitats in recent years, a feature which may just be discerned on the map. It has, for instance, shown a liking for young conifer plantations — as on Bridgham Heath. In addition, there has been a gradual exploitation of dry ditches in farmland, well away from rivers, streams and open water: these ditches are especially favoured when they contain an abundance of such plants as willow herb, such a site having been located by the B1077 road at Winfarthing. Finally, nesting in rape fields was reported by two NBBS observers.

RM.

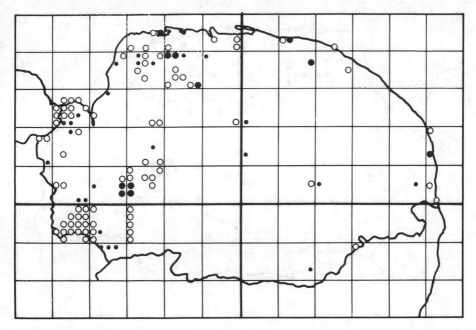

Corn Bunting

Miliaria calandra

Tetrads recorded in:	117	(8%)
Possible breeding:	26	(22%)
Probable breeding:	80	(68%)
Confirmed breeding:	11	(9%)

This species has an irregular breeding range, both nationally and in Norfolk. Seago, writing in 1967 (*Birds of Norfolk*), observed that it was resident in most coastal parishes, widespread in the Fens, and that isolated colonies existed from time to time in Breckland. Such a distribution seems to have obtained over the 1968-1972 period of the BTO/IWC *Atlas* (as plotted on a 10-km square grid), but the NBBS has subsequently determined a general contraction of this. Between 1980 and 1985, only scattered pockets of Corn Buntings were found around the coast, while in the Fens they were only widespread between the former A17 road and the Wash in the north and between the Ouse Washes and the A10 road in the south. Open, chalky fields with a scattering of scrub beyond the western and northern limits of Breckland, as well as similar country in North-west Norfolk, held good numbers, but none was found in the Brecks proper. A handful of records from central Norfolk may only relate to wandering, non-breeding birds.

Breeding is hard to confirm for this species, but most probable records in districts where it was found in good numbers should have related to this.

Subtle factors seem likely to determine choice of breeding habitat, as witness its range in the peat Fens (which were not for the most part surveyed until 1985, admittedly). In Hilgay Fen, males sang from almost every field gate-post and telegraph pole; in the ostensibly similar Upwell and Methwold Fens only a few birds were recorded.

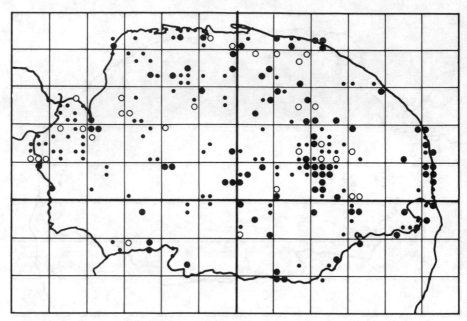

Feral Pigeon

Columba livia

Tetrads recorded in:	240	(16%)
Possible breeding:	125	(52%)
Probable breeding:	30	(13%)
Confirmed breeding:	85	(35%)

Only one example of the true Rock Dove, the predecessor of the Feral Pigeon, has ever been recorded in Norfolk. There was some debate during the planning of the NBBS as to whether the feral bird should be given a place on the recording cards. It was, however, decided that this is an obvious component of the county's avifauna and that it would be justifiable to map its breeding distribution. In any case this is a bird which is greatly appreciated by many people who come to enjoy its company in urban parks.

This bird is as would be expected concentrated in towns, including virtually all of the smaller ones. The largest population is focussed upon Greater Norwich, and the map suggests an overflow from there into the surrounding country districts.

Church towers and farm buildings account for most of the records in rural areas. It is virtually certain that this bird occurs in such locations in other tetrads, but was perhaps absent-mindedly overlooked by observers.

Additional species

The following thirty species include rarities or semi-rarities which cannot be mapped for security reasons, and others (which in some cases are also sensitive) for which breeding was not actually confirmed during the NBBS.

Then comes an entry for Wood Duck, which is listed Category D by the British Ornithologists' Union as there is doubt that it has ever occurred in Britain in a truly wild state. Finally, the Muscovy Duck is listed — a bird which has yet to be placed on any 'official' British list.

Bittern   Botaurus stellaris

Tetrads recorded in:	12	(<1%)
Possible breeding:	3	(25%)
Probable breeding:	5	(42%)
Confirmed breeding:	4	(33%)

A rare resident of Norfolk's more extensive reed-beds, which is rather more widespread in its occurrence during the winter months. A once familiar bird throughout the county's major wetland complexes, this population became extinct in the mid-19th century — thanks to drainage schemes, and the predation by 'sportsmen' and egg-collectors — but was to become re-established to a limited extent in the early 20th century. A slow recovery through to 1954, when there were up to sixty booming (territorial) males, was followed by a decline. During the NBBS, the number of such males did not rise above the low teens in any year; however, it does appear that the population may now have stabilised at about this level.

This species is protected in Great Britain at all times by special penalties under Schedule 1, Part I of the Wildlife and Countryside Act, 1981.

Mandarin   Aix galericulata

There is unlikely to be a self-perpetuating population of this duck in the county, and records which were submitted by NBBS workers are likely to have related to escapes from collections. One record of confirmed breeding came from tree roots on a slope overlooking the Yare Valley at Bramerton; a record of probable breeding came from Sandringham Park; and a record of possible breeding emanated from the Wensum in Norwich.

Garganey   Anas querquedula

Tetrads recorded in:	21	(1%)
Possible breeding:	11	(52%)
Probable breeding:	3	(14%)
Confirmed breeding:	7	(33%)

A rare and erratic summer visitor to Broadland, the north coast and the Fens. The breeding population of this attractive little duck, which was never large, has declined since the 1950s; indeed, it is unlikely that more than a handful of pairs bred in any single year of the NBBS. Further facts concerning its recent and current status must be withheld for security reasons.

This species is protected in Great Britain at all times by special penalties under Schedule 1, Part I of the Wildlife and Countryside Act, 1981.

Eier

Somateria mollissima

A regular visitor to Norfolk coastal waters, a few mostly immature birds summer in The Wash and off the north coast. Breeding has never been suspected here, but a displaying male was noted off the trial bund in The Wash (tetrad TF52A) by a NBBS worker. In view of the southwards expansion of its range this century, notably into Holland, future colonisation of certain stretches of the Norfolk coast is a possibility.

Ruddy Duck

Oxyura jamaicensis

No self-sustaining feral population of this introduced species has become established in the county, and records submitted during the NBBS are likely to relate to escapes from collections. Records of probable breeding were noted at a Flegg Broad and at Hardley Flood; one of possible breeding was submitted from Hillington Lake.

Honey Buzzard

Pernis apivorus

This handsome raptor, which occurs in small numbers as a passage migrant, actually bred in a well-wooded district in the county in 1970 and 1974. Four records of possible breeding in suitable habitat were submitted by NBBS observers; it is all but certain that breeding did not take place here during the course of this project.

This species is protected in Great Britain at all times by special penalties under Schedule 1, Part I of the Wildlife and Countryside Act, 1981.

Marsh Harrier

Circus aeruginosus

Tetrads recorded in:	46	(3%)
Possible breeding:	38	(83%)
Probable breeding:	4	(9%)
Confirmed breeding:	4	(9%)

A scarce summer visitor, somewhat more widespread as a passage migrant and winter visitor. This superb raptor bred successfully in each NBBS season, with totals of between 24 and 49 young reaching the flying stage. Norfolk remains its British stronghold. Despite this apparently optimistic state of affairs, largely brought about through the careful protection of sites such as the well-publicised RSPB Strumpshaw Reserve, this bird remains sensitive to disturbance and for this reason it has not been mapped. Nevertheless, readers may be directed to articles by Norman Sills in the *Norfolk Bird Reports* for 1983 and 1984, pp.342-348 and 85-94 respectively.

This species is protected in Great Britain at all times by special penalties under Schedule 1, Part I of the Wildlife and Countryside Act, 1981.

Hen Harrier

Circus cyaneus

A generally scarce winter visitor and passage migrant, which was once a breeding resident of Broadland — where the last Norfolk nest was found in 1861 — and Fenland. One record of its occurrence during the NBBS was regarded as having constituted probable breeding.

This species is protected in Great Britain at all times by special penalties under Schedule 1, Part I of the Wildlife and Countryside Act, 1981.

Montagu's Harrier

Circus pygargus

A rare summer visitor and passage migrant. During the NBBS, successful breeding by single pairs in 1983 and 1984 and by two pairs in 1985. Total NBBS records amounted to confirmed breeding in two tetrads and possible breeding in four others.

Such is the sensitivity of this species that no further information can be released here.

This species is protected in Great Britain at all times by special penalties under Schedule 1, Part I of the Wildlife and Countryside Act, 1981.

Goshawk

Accipiter gentilis

A former vagrant which has become a more frequent visitor in recent years, although it must be stated that some birds are accidental or deliberate releases from falconers' stock. Breeding occurred at one site annually from 1975 to 1980 — the first year of the NBBS — and at another locality in the same district in 1985.

This species is protected in Great Britain at all times by special penalties under Schedule 1, Part I of the Wildlife and Countryside Act, 1981.

Buzzard

Buteo buteo

A scarce visitor to the county, more usual as a passage migrant and winter visitor although it may occur in any month. Successful breeding is not known to have occurred since the earlier 19th century; a pair built a nest in a West Norfolk locality in 1984, but no eggs were laid — and in any case one of the birds was a falconer's escape. A record of possible breeding from a site in the east of the county was also submitted by a NBBS observer.

Hobby

Falco subbuteo

A scarce passage migrant and, usually, non-breeding summer visitor. Two young which were raised at a West Norfolk site in 1985 provided the county with its first successful breeding record since 1933. In addition, one probable and five possible breeding records were submitted during the NBBS.

This species is protected in Great Britain at all times by special penalties under Schedule 1, Part 1 of the Wildlife and Countryside Act, 1981.

Lady Amherst's Pheasant Chrysolophus amherstiae

It is unlikely that the county holds a self-perpetuating population of this colourful introduced species. Successful breeding occurred at Guist and Quidenham in 1973, but nothing more appears to have been recorded concerning this bird there. Two records of possible breeding during the NBBS, from Bergh Apton and Hassingham in East Norfolk, almost certainly concerned escapes from collections.

Stone-curlew Burhinus oedicnemus

Tetrads recorded in:	32	(2%)
Possible breeding:	10	(31%)
Probable breeding:	11	(34%)
Confirmed breeding:	11	(34%)

This summer visitor was once such a distinctive feature of the brecks, heaths and stony open fields of the county that it was accorded the alternative name of Norfolk Plover. Although some of its habitat vanished during the afforestation of many Breckland heaths during the inter-war years, a few displaced birds were sufficiently adaptable as to take to nesting in forest rides. A decline in its population from the 1950s seems to have coincided with endemic myxomatosis taking a heavy toll of the rabbits which once maintained the close-cropped turf preferred by the Stone-curlew in many of its breeding areas. In addition, agricultural operations during the breeding season and the predations of egg-collectors have furthered the Stone-curlew's decline. Conservation bodies and individuals having a particular concern for this bird's well-being have asked that there be no further discussion of it in the *Norfolk Bird Atlas*, save to state that all records received came from the western half of the county — mainly from the Brecks.

This species is protected in Great Britain at all times by special penalties under Schedule 1, Part 1 of the Wildlife and Countryside Act, 1981.

Kentish Plover Charadrius alexandrinus

A scarce passage migrant, more rarely observed at other times. The first ever attempt at breeding in Norfolk came in 1983, when two clutches of eggs laid by a single pair at a north coast site are known not to have hatched.

This species is protected in Great Britain at all times by special penalties under Schedule 1, Part I of the Wildlife and Countryside Act, 1981.

Ruff Philomachus pugnax

Once an established breeding bird in the major wetlands of the county, this population became extinct after 1890. After isolated instances in 1907 and 1922, nesting again occurred in 1970 at a Fenland location and has probably taken place there in a number of subsequent years. A record of probable breeding was submitted by a NBBS worker from a north coast site.

This species is protected in Great Britain at all times by special penalties under Schedule 1, Part I of the Wildlife and Countryside Act, 1981.

Black-tailed Godwit

Limosa limosa

This wader bred widely in the major wetland complexes of Norfolk until the early 19th century, but has since tended to occur for the most part as a passage migrant. However, successful nesting in Fenland which commenced in 1953 has since been an annual occurrence. Breeding has subsequently happened elsewhere in the county, including one north coast site in 1980 — the first year of the NBBS. In all, confirmed breeding was noted in five tetrads.

This species is protected in Great Britain at all times by special penalties under Schedule 1, Part I of the Wildlife and Countryside Act, 1981.

Green Sandpiper

Tringa ochropus

Most common as a passage migrant, this bird can occur in the county at any season. Breeding has never been proved here, but was considered possible in two tetrads in West Norfolk and in another in the east of the county by observers.

This species is protected in Great Britain at all times by special penalties under Schedule 1, Part I of the Wildlife and Countryside Act, 1981.

Common Sandpiper

Tringa hypoleucos

Most common as a passage migrant, it is occasional in winter and also as a generally non-breeding summer visitor. Prior to the NBBS, breeding occurred at five scattered localities in the county between 1898 and 1963. The first year of this project, 1980, witnessed two successful nesting records: one from a gravel pit on the eastern margin of the Fens, and the other from an upper reach of an East Norfolk river. Six records of possible breeding were submitted by observers: four from inland rivers and streams, one from a Fenland drain, and one from the southern margin of The Wash.

Kittiwake

Rissa tridactyla

This coastal nesting gull is present throughout the year in Norfolk, and has made a number of successful nesting attempts from 1946 to 1974 at places along both north and east coasts. During the NBBS, just one record of possible breeding was submitted — from Happisburgh.

Woodlark

Lullula arborea

Tetrads recorded in:	10	(<1%)
Possible breeding:	5	(50%)
Probable breeding:	3	(30%)
Confirmed breeding:	2	(20%)

The above statistics of this rare and decreasing Norfolk resident are set down in the knowledge that this is one of but two species for which records are known to have been withheld from the *Norfolk Bird Atlas*. Save for two records of possible breeding from contiguous tetrads in North-west Norfolk, this bird is now confined to woodland margins which for the most part abut onto heathland in Breckland. In view of the incomplete information and the sensitivity of this species it has not been mapped.

This species is protected in Great Britain at all times by special penalties under Schedule 1, Part I of the Wildlife and Countryside Act, 1981.

Fieldfare

Turdus pilaris

An often abundant passage migrant and winter visitor, a few Fieldfares linger in the county until late spring. Such birds would, it may be assumed, account for the twelve scattered records of possible breeding submitted by NBBS observers; however, a pair seen displaying at Cranworth were regarded as constituting a valid record of probable breeding. Successful nesting has never been established in Norfolk.

This species is protected in Great Britain at all times by special penalties under Schedule 1, Part I of the Wildlife and Countryside Act, 1981.

Redwing

Turdus iliacus

Just like its close relative the Fieldfare, the Redwing is often abundant as a passage migrant and winter visitor and will sometimes linger in the county until well into spring. Four possible breeding records submitted almost certainly related to birds delaying their spring flight to Scandinavia; however, records of singing birds at Carbrooke and Grimston were regarded as constituting probable breeding. Nesting in Norfolk has never been proved, though.

This species is protected in Great Britain at all times by special penalties under Schedule 1, Part I of the Wildlife and Countryside Act, 1981.

Savi's Warbler

Locustella luscinioides

This once common summer visitor to extensive reed-beds in the county became extinct in the mid-19th century. This population was considered to have been driven away by drainage schemes; however, surviving wetlands have again attracted this bird in small numbers from 1967. Breeding was first proved after this re-colonisation in 1981, and is likely to occur annually in especially favoured sites. Breeding was proved in two tetrads and regarded as probable in six others, but locations are not revealed.

This species is protected in Great Britain at all times by special penalties under Schedule 1, Part I of the Wildlife and Countryside Act, 1981.

Firecrest

Regulus ignicapillus

A regular although somewhat scarce passage migrant, this tiny bird also occurs in small numbers in both winter and summer. The first breeding record for Norfolk for which full details were made available concerned a pair which nested in a Norwich cemetery in 1984; it is also known that another pair bred successfully in Breckland during the NBBS. Elsewhere, two records which constituted probable breeding as well as three possible ones, were forthcoming. It is likely that further instances of at least presence during recent breeding seasons have passed unnoticed by observers.

This species is protected in Great Britain at all times by special penalties under Schedule 1, Part I of the Wildlife and Countryside Act, 1981.

Pied Flycatcher

Ficedula hypoleuca

This bird is normally only known as a passage migrant in Eastern England south of Flamborough Head, so there was considerable interest expressed in the pair at a location on the Cromer-Holt ridge which provided Norfolk with its first definite breeding record in 1978. Such an instance has not been known to occur subsequently, although NBBS workers submitted two records each of possible and probable breeding.

Golden Oriole

Oriolus oriolus

Tetrads recorded in:	21	(1%)
Possible breeding:	3	(14%)
Probable breeding:	12	(57%)
Confirmed breeding:	6	(29%)

A scarce passage migrant and, since 1971, a rare summer visitor which has bred with slowly increasing regularity and is gradually expanding its range. This recent colonist must still be regarded as sensitive to both accidental and illegal disturbance; it has therefore been decided that no map will be published.

This species is protected in Great Britain at all times by special penalties under Schedule 1, Part I of the Wildlife and Countryside Act, 1981.

Red-backed Shrike

Lanius collurio

A rapidly declining summer visitor to heaths and marginal land; also a passage migrant. It is possible that the NBBS has coincided with this bird's last seasons of being a regular breeder here. However, the point that three records each of confirmed and probable breeding — all from different 10-km squares — were submitted has to be stated alongside the fact that the identity of two further sites where breeding occurred was kept from the NBBS.

This species is protected in Great Britain at all times by special penalties under Schedule 1, Part I of the Wildlife and Countryside Act, 1981.

Serin

Serinus serinus

A vagrant to the county, although signs of a light spring passage have been discerned from 1975. NBBS observers submitted two records of probable breeding and one of possible breeding from West Norfolk sites; none of the birds concerned are known to have paired, but as this is a species which has been on the point of colonising England since successful nesting occurred in Dorset in 1967 they seem worthy of mention in the *Norfolk Bird Atlas*.

This species is protected in Great Britain at all times by special penalties under Schedule 1, Part I of the Wildlife and Countryside Act, 1981.

Parrot Crossbill

Loxia pytyopsittacus

Hitherto a vagrant from Scandinavia, a pair of these birds nested in a pinewood at Wells-next-the-Sea in both 1984 and 1985. Fuller details are given in the *Norfolk Bird Reports*, for 1984 and 1985, pp.98-102 and 256-259 respectively.

This species is protected in Great Britain at all times by special penalties under Schedule 1, Part I of the Wildlife and Countryside Act, 1981.

Wood Duck

Aix sponsa

Records of this bird are taken to represent escapes from collections: indeed, it is listed as a Category D species by the British Ornithologists' Union for this reason. An instance of confirmed breeding in the TF63 10-km square during the BTO/IWC *Atlas* project of 1968-1972 was not recorded in any *Norfolk Bird Report* for those years; one assumes it was not seen as an event of any consequence locally. During the NBBS a single record of possible breeding was submitted from the Wensum at Bylaugh.

Muscovy Duck

Cairina moschata

A record of confirmed breeding from West Somerton and another of possible breeding from Burgh-next-Aylsham were placed in the NBBS files for future reference, despite the fact that they must have related to escapes and that this species does not have a place on any official list of British Birds.

Index